SEX AND SANITY

Sex and Sanity

~~~~~~

Melvin Anchell, M.D.

The Macmillan Company, New York, New York
Collier-Macmillan Limited, London

The Macmillan Company
866 Third Avenue, New York, N.Y. 10022
Collier-Macmillan Canada Ltd., Toronto, Ontario
Library of Congress Catalog Card Number: 73-158166
First Printing
Printed in the United States of America

Dedicated to
my patients who have allowed me to share
their innermost feelings

Contents

∿∿∿∿∿∿∿∿∿∿∿∿∿∿∿∿∿∿∿∿∿

SECTION TWO—PERVERSITY

SECTION THREE—OBSCENITY AND
PORNOGRAPHY

SECTION ONE

Profile of Love

I

~~~~~~~~~~~~~~~~~~~~~~~~~~~~~~~~~~~~

A Bucket of
Chicken Feathers

During my senior year in medical school at the University
of Maryland I drew the unwelcome assignment of being on
emergency OB (obstetrics) call on New Year's Eve. My
disappointment was acute, because I had a very special date
for the fraternity dance that night. I was fourth on the call
list, however, and as the afternoon dragged on uneventfully,
I began to hope that I might be able to celebrate after all.

But babies are no respecters of a doctor's convenience.
At 5:00 P.M. the calls began to come in rapid succession
—and by 5:30 P.M. I was trudging through the winter twi-
light toward the streetcar stop, lugging my hospital suitcase
of sterilized sheets, towels, drapes, instruments, rubber gloves,
and so on. This would be my first delivery in a home and on
my own. I tried to allay my nervousness with the reminder
that medical students were never sent out on complicated
cases. This one was a sixth pregnancy with a history of five
completely normal births.

In an upstairs room at the end of a dingy row of houses,
I found my patient already in labor on a unclean bed,
surrounded by six or seven chanting women. At a few stern
words from the young doctor they dispersed, only the

wizened midwife remained at my request. She helped me to set a medically correct stage for the baby's arrival. And just in time. As I slipped on my sterile gloves and peered beneath the sterile drapes, the baby's head popped through the vagina. Within ten minutes, with scarcely any assistance from me, he was squirming on the sterile towels and sheets and lustily protesting as I cut and tied the umbilical cord and handed him over to the midwife.

With a light heart I prepared for the finale, the ejection of the placenta or afterbirth, a supposedly simple procedure. If this went as well as the baby's delivery, I could easily keep my date for the dance. As I had been instructed, I made a slight manipulation and applied the appropriate pressure. Nothing happened. In such an event, I had been taught to wait ten minutes and try again. I did. Again nothing. When another thirty minutes went by to no avail, I began to have all sorts of apprehensions. Perhaps the placenta was attached to the uterus, a severe complication that could only be treated in the hospital and that sometimes threatened the mother's life.

By this time the baby was blissfully sleeping after the midwife's expert ministrations, and the old woman was watching me anxiously. At my query, she told me there was a pay telephone in the downstairs hall. I called the resident obstetrician at the hospital. Attributing the difficulty to my inexperience, he rather brusquely told me to "give it more time." I gave it another thirty minutes—and still nothing happened.

At this point the old midwife excused herself and went out. About five minutes later she reappeared with a bucket half filled with chicken feathers.

"What in the world?" I exclaimed. "Get that stuff out of here! Do you want to add to the complications by contaminating everything?"

"I jes' wants to help, Doctor," she explained earnestly. "Effen you'll jes' let me git dis woman off de bed and onto dis here bucket o' chicken feathers, hit'll all be over in no time."

Thoroughly exasperated, I gave the old woman a rapid, impromptu lecture on the dangers of infection, and also informed her (according to the teaching of the mid-1940s) that the patient was not to get out of bed for ten days.

"Now take that bucket of dirty feathers and throw it away!" I concluded.

Shaking her head in protest, she reluctantly complied. Dejectedly I called my date and told her to go on to the dance with another couple, and that I would join them later if I could. Then I called the hospital again, begging them to send an ambulance for the patient. Three phone calls and several hours later, the resident physician finally gave in. By that time it was 12:00 P.M. and I felt more in need of the ambulance than my patient did. Meticulously following the medical tradition of that day, we eased her onto the stretcher, carefully keeping her flat on her back.

But when we wheeled her into the delivery room, my patient—no doubt thoroughly bored with the whole thing by now—did not follow the instructions to slide onto the table. She stood up. And plop! Out came the afterbirth into a bucket that was fortunately there. Obviously the placenta had been lodged in the woman's long vagina, which had been stretched by the six previous deliveries. When she stood up, it did what came naturally—obeyed the laws of gravity and expelled itself.

By the time I left the hospital, even the streetcars of Baltimore had gone to bed. As I plodded dispiritedly through the snow toward my lonely room, I reflected upon the ironies of life, and of the medical profession in particular. The old midwife with her bucket of chicken feathers would have done a much better job than I did. In addition to the force of gravity, the feathers would have tickled the patient's thighs, causing a spontaneous muscular contraction that would have expelled the afterbirth and all its remnants in one piece. The cushion of feathers would have received it gently and absorbed the blood. Afterward, the vagina could have been cleansed antiseptically to avert infection. And I could have gone to the New Year's Eve dance!

Today, the scientific equivalent of a bucket of chicken feathers has been a long accepted procedure throughout the medical profession. Getting the mother onto her feet shortly after delivery of the baby has proved to be the best method of preventing blood clots, milk legs, and other complications. As with so many things, we have come full circle and returned to nature's way.

The lesson that was brought home to me on that cold, bitter New Year's Eve has remained with me ever since. As a neuropsychiatrist in the U.S. Army, as a family physician for many years in Houston, Texas, and currently in Los Angeles, California, clinical proof has been my criterion. No matter how fine or how absurd a theory (new or old) may sound, its real worth is determined by its practical application. How does it work with my patients? And why?

More than twenty years of experience with many thousands of patients have led me to the inevitable conclusion that if a medicine or a treatment works in accord with nature —if it aids or reinforces the natural processes of health and healing—it is beneficial. If it works against nature, it is harmful. This principle applies psychologically as well as physically.

It is particularly important in regard to the sexual life of the human being. In this connection, the principle of following natural law applies to every aspect of a person's life, because everything that happens from the moment of birth influences one's sexual adjustment. And one's sexual adjustment, in turn, influences everything that a human being does.

Today we are troubled about the increase in crime, violence, divorce, moral laxity, general unrest, dissatisfaction, and just plain unhappiness. These conditions are prevalent among both juveniles and adults throughout our society. Why should this be, when our lauded "sexual emancipation" is supposed to give us release from all tensions? Isn't everybody "doing what comes naturally"? Why, then, should mankind be plagued with more tensions than ever?

There are, of course, many contributing factors. But the root of the difficulty, it seems to me, is the fact that the sexual life of human beings is becoming more and more unnatural.

We are not cats or dogs or even chimpanzees. We are humans, and human nature is psychosomatic—composed of both mind and body. Sigmund Freud, the father of modern psychiatry, must be whirling in his grave at the misinterpretations of his teachings that are being promulgated today as sexual gospel by the vast majority of sexperts. The sex act in its physical aspect alone not only does not bring complete satisfaction, it actually creates more tension than it relieves. The psychological component of sexuality outweighs the physical in men and especially in women. That's the way nature made us, and when we thwart nature, we're in for trouble.

Distortion of human sexuality is, I am convinced, one of the major causes of the overall sickness of our society. This diagnosis is based upon my intimate knowledge of the sexual misinformation of my patients and its influence on their lives and health—mental and emotional, as well as physical. The experienced family physician is in a unique position to learn these facts, because he is concerned with each patient as a total human being—not just his heart or his lungs or his appendix. A physician who has a close rapport with his patient, and is interested in his emotional and his physical needs, finds it possible to detect and often to prevent an acute condition, which may range from major surgery to divorce. The mind and body cannot be cut into two parts. Organic conditions can cause psychological problems; and

emotional distress can cause organic illnesses, which are used
as a relief from the mental tension.

A patient who comes in for a headache, for example, may
really want to talk about his or her marital difficulties. The
teen-ager, whom the family physician delivered and took
care of throughout childhood, often confides more freely in
his doctor than in his parents. Grandparents, too, ask for
advice about real or fancied sex complications that accompany
aging.

Each case, of course, has its individual variations. Certain
patterns, however, continue to repeat themselves, and it is
these that form the basis of this book. The cases presented
are authentic and typical, although identifying details have
been disguised. They have been selected in an effort to help
the reader to distinguish between beneficial and harmful
sexuality.

There is no magical cure-all—in spite of the panaceas
offered by the sexperts. A clear understanding of the actual
"facts of life," however, should serve as a strong antidote
to these quack nostrums, as well as a protection against the
psychological venereal diseases that perverted minds are
currently spreading through mass media. Sick themselves,
these purveyors of perversion are making the unnatural appear
normal.

II

~~~~~~

Sex and Love—
The Young Couple

To my astonishment, Patty suddenly burst into tears. She
was sitting in the patient's chair beside my desk, as she had
on innumerable visits before. This time it was her youngest
child whom she was bringing in for an immunization shot.
The baby, wiggling contentedly on her lap, was not Patty's
problem, it was her husband.

"Dr. Anchell," she sobbed, "please help me! It's Bob—I
don't know what to do!"

"What's the matter with Bob?" I asked.

"I don't know if it's Bob or me." Patty was trying hard
to hold back the tears. "I don't think he l-loves m-me any
m-more. And I'm not sure if I-I love him. Oh, it's awful!"
She wept unrestrainedly.

This was the first inkling I had had of any difficulty between Patty and Bob. It had been about seven years ago
that Patty had come to my office with her first pregnancy.
She had been only seventeen then—an extremely attractive
girl, apparently very much in love with her young husband
and happy to be bearing his child. The oldest daughter of
a large family, she had been taken for granted as the household "slave" during her childhood and early teens. To get
married and have a home of her own, with someone who

9

considered her the most important person in the world, was the fulfillment of Patty's most cherished dream.

When I first met Bob, he had seemed the typically proud young father. He obviously felt that in Patty he had found his dream girl, who satisfied his need for affectionate understanding as well as his natural sex desires. He was a fine-looking young man of about twenty, even-tempered and pleasant, with a good job and a sense of responsibility.

Since then my professional services had been in regular demand for the normal problems of childbearing and child rearing. There were four little ones now, the youngest about six months old. Patty was a good homemaker and Bob a good provider. Both loved children and wanted a large family, so the burdens of parenthood were not unwelcome. It should have been an ideal marriage. During the past two years I had noticed that Patty was becoming tense and nervous, but that could be expected in a young mother with four babies to look after. I had been giving her the sort of general reassurance that seemed to satisfy her. Whenever I asked about Bob, she always replied cheerfully. So this present outburst came as a complete surprise.

Disturbed by his mother's weeping, the baby started to whimper. Automatically Patty soothed him, and her own tears began to subside. She dried her eyes, blew her nose, and looked up at me pleadingly.

"I know I'm being terribly emotional, Doctor, and please forgive me. But it's gotten to the point now where if I don't talk to someone, I'll go crazy. And you're the only one I can talk to about this."

"What's the trouble, Patty?" I asked.

"It's—it's—" Patty hesitated, then took a deep breath and plunged on. "I might just as well say it right out—it's sex. I don't enjoy it any more. Bob wants it all the time—but I—I—well, there must be something wrong with me. Or with Bob. Or with us. Something's happened. I don't know what it is! All I know is that having sex makes me all tense and nervous—just the opposite of what it's supposed to do. And that makes Bob all upset. We quarrel all the time now. He thinks I don't love him. I do—but—that is, I thought I did. But he keeps on telling me I don't love him, until now I'm beginning to believe him! Dr. Anchell, can you help me?"

That afternoon began a series of discussions, which continued for several visits. Although Patty's problem was new and distressing to her, it was one that I have encountered over and over again in my practice.

When Patty and Bob were first married, their sexual relations had seemed to be mutually enjoyable. Although Patty never did get as excited as Bob, she liked it when he kissed and caressed her. Whenever he did—even when he'd just come home from work—he wanted to go to bed with her right away. This embarrassed her, and she usually managed to postpone it until bedtime. There she enjoyed the lovemaking, and Bob was so passionately happy having intercourse with her that it made her feel happy, too.

It was different, however, after the babies came along. Patty's apparent interest in sex gradually diminished, until finally the sex act became distasteful to her. Her attitude was not helped by Bob's constant nagging. He would complain about her watching TV instead of washing his shirts or because the children's playthings were scattered around, or accuse her of neglecting the children, the housekeeping, and so on. Patty, who prided herself on her domestic talents, felt that Bob's criticism was completely unjustified. At first she took it without complaint, thinking that perhaps Bob was tired or had been upset by something at the shop. He would then become contrite, pet her, and they would make up in bed. This seemed to satisfy Bob—but not Patty.

As she became more tense, so did he. They began to quarrel. Afterwards, when Bob tried the usual conciliation, Patty could not make herself respond.

"I tried—Lord knows I tried!" she told me. "But all I

wanted to do was to get up out of bed and forget all about
sex."

This, of course, infuriated Bob. He accused Patty of not
loving him—and, finally, of having affairs with other men.
The more deeply he hurt her by these unwarranted accusations, the more Patty's affection for him waned and sexual
intercourse became unpleasant. She had taken up smoking
in an attempt to relax her tensions and had gone through
agonies of self-reproach in the belief that something was the
matter with her, that she was not "all woman." Lately,
however, she had begun to question whether it was her fault,
after all. Perhaps with "the right partner" she might respond
sexually. Then, a few nights before her outburst in my office,
she discovered that Bob was having an affair with another
woman.

These were the outward, conscious aspects of Patty's
dilemma, the symptoms of a sick marriage. The cause, however, was in underlying, subconscious events.

Patty and Bob, like most of their contemporaries, had been
indoctrinated with the misinformation that men and women
naturally have the same unbridled passion for sex and that
women need only to shed outmoded inhibitions and really
let go in order to match or even outdo their men at mating.

In trying to live up to the fictional ideal of the passionate
young bride, Patty at first deluded both herself and Bob
into believing that she enjoyed the genital sex act. As we
frankly discussed it, however, Patty came to realize that she
really derived her pleasure from the affectionate petting
and from the love she felt for Bob. Satisfying his sex needs
and providing for him as a wife gratified her normal feminine
needs and brought them closer. In this way the sex act was
important to her. Her idealism of Bob was not inseparably
entwined with erotic feelings—she admitted that she never
could understand why he got so sensually excited about the
sex act. In the beginning of their married life she had an

echo of his ecstasy, because of the joy in his intense wanting of her and in her pleasing him.

She tried to please him and show her love in other ways as well—being a companion, keeping the house clean, cooking his favorite dishes, and looking her prettiest to greet him when he came home from work. What she wanted most from Bob was his affectionate love, his appreciation of her as a *person*. Not having the same physical need for the sex act as he did, she could not understand the urgency of his desire. Nor did she realize that Bob was using this means to express his affectionate as well as his sensual love for her. She began to feel that her only attraction for him was physical and that he did not really love her as she wanted to be loved. Patty had not analyzed the situation this way before, of course, but her understanding grew as we talked it over.

Patty's indifference to the sex act was increased by conscious expressions of mounting frustration and resentment in her marriage—just as Bob's nagging was a subconscious retaliation for his feeling of rejection. When Patty took his criticism without complaint, he felt reassured that she really did love him. Otherwise she would not have put up with it. His masculine ego restored, he felt sorry for abusing her and tried to show it by making love to her. Then the vicious cycle began all over again—and became more aggravated by repetition.

As Patty's sexual response grew colder, Bob's accusations grew hotter. When she answered back and they quarreled, he became convinced that she did not love him—and finally that she was unfaithful to him. Beneath this was the subconscious fear that he was not man enough to arouse his wife sexually. So in order to "prove his manhood," he found another sex partner. Patty, with similar subconscious doubts and fears, was at the point of considering adultery herself in an effort to discover the right partner to whom she could respond sexually. Neither of them understood what was really the matter.

After our discussions concerning human sexuality (see graph, on page 47), Patty faced and accepted the actual facts of life—that it was perfectly natural and normal for her and Bob to have opposite attitudes toward the sex act, and that she was not supposed to have a climax every time he did. As a matter of fact, Patty had never experienced an orgasm.

"But how did I get pregnant, then?" she asked.

"You don't have to have an orgasm to get pregnant," I explained. "Every time Bob has a climax with you, he does, however, have an orgasm and ejects sperm. If one of these sperm connects with an ovum, or egg, of yours, it fertilizes that egg and you get pregnant. It has nothing to do with whether you have or don't have a climax during the sex act. It simply depends on whether you have intercourse at the time of the month you're expelling an egg from your ovaries.

"Later on, you will no doubt experience climaxes and have orgasms," I continued. "Most women do after the age of twenty-five. How old are you now, Patty? Twenty-four?"

She nodded.

"You're an average, normal, healthy young woman. So in another year or two you should experience your first real orgasm. Then you'll begin to understand what the sex act will mean to you and better appreciate what it means to your husband. It's the reason many women say they truly fell in love with their husbands after they were married. And, perhaps, you will fall in love with Bob all over again."

"But that'll be too late," protested Patty. "He's—he's already having it with that other woman. If I'm going to get him back, I've got to do it now."

"Patty, if you were reassured that Bob truly loves you— and that he is having this outside affair only to salvage his pride because he feels that you have rejected him—you could begin to love Bob affectionately again and enjoy the sex act with him in the same way that you did when you were first married. Couldn't you?"

Patty was thoughtfully silent for a few moments. "Yes," she decided. "If I know Bob loved me—for myself, not just for sex —I'm sure I would feel differently about it. But—does he?"

"I believe he does, Patty," I assured her. "He simply doesn't understand the situation."

"I hope you're right," she sighed. "Will you talk to him?"

"I'll be glad to. Tell him to come in and see me after work."

My diagnosis of Bob's problem proved to be correct. He was diffident at first and inclined to resent the fact that Patty had "bothered" me with their "private affair." However, when he discovered that my attitude was not one of criticism but of detached sympathy and understanding, he seemed relieved to be able to unburden himself.

Believing as he did that Patty had the same intense physical urge for sex as he had, Bob could account for her coldness in only one way—she had ceased to love him. If she loved him, she would want it as much as he did. There was also the nagging doubt of his own prowess—that perhaps he couldn't satisfy her. He had decided to find out.

Ever since the trouble with Patty began, Bob had been spending evenings in the local bar drinking with the fellows and flirting with the women who hung around. But he couldn't bring himself to pick up a barfly. Somehow it seemed different with Goldie, the cashier at the shop. After all, she wasn't like the girls at the bar, he knew her at work. She seemed to like Bob, so he started playing up to her. There was no mistaking her invitation to go further.

"It wasn't that I fell in love with her, or anything like that," Bob told me. "I've always loved Patty. But—well, it got pretty obvious that Patty didn't love me. She'd stay up nights watching TV until I went to sleep. Or if that didn't work, she'd make some excuse or another. If we did have sex, it was empty—like she felt nothing, nothing at all. So figure how that made me feel. After all, how much can a guy take?"

So Bob dated Goldie. And—he had to admit—she really did know how to haxe sexual intercourse and make love. The drinks were set out when he arrived and she snuggled up to him while they sipped. He had the feeling she wanted to as much as he—something Patty never did. She undid his tie, unbuckled his belt and showed her desire for him before going to bed. In bed, she made him feel like the great lover she said he was. She made little moaning and whimpering sounds of ecstasy and really seemed to enjoy his lovemaking capabilities.

There was certainly nothing wrong with him sexually, Bob decided. It must be Patty. He remembered Joe talking about how his wife "played around" while he was at work, and had "nothing left" for him when they went to bed at night. That must be what Patty was doing. Bob felt insulted and furious. Here he was bringing in a good paycheck, giving Patty and the kids everything they needed—and this was how she repaid him!

Because his relations with Goldie seemed to prove the thesis that women have the same passions as men, it was difficult for Bob to believe otherwise. He listened to me politely, but skeptically, as I explained the natural facts to him.

"You mean to tell me that Patty is the mother of four children and she's never had an orgasm?" he asked incredulously.

"That's true, Bob," I affirmed. "Any woman can have a child after she matures physically. But most women don't mature sexually, in the sensual sense, until their middle or late twenties."

I told him that among my patients were swingers like Goldie, and that their honest reactions to sex were part of the data on which my graph was based.

"Actually, these amateur prostitutes—like most of their professional sisters—are even more frustrated sexually than the men they go to bed with," I explained. "The men at least get a physical release. Most of these women don't.

They learn how to simulate reaching a climax in the sex act—to prove their value by making the man of the moment feel like a great lover, as you say. In return they receive re-assurance, money, gifts, popularity, or other such rewards, which serve as a substitute for the affectionate love that each woman subconsciously longs for.

"Every woman wants to be loved completely," I pointed out. "First with affection and appreciation of herself as an individual—and only secondarily as a partner in the genital sex act. For an average man, physical love is easier than for an average woman. But love for a man is also incomplete without both components."

Bob admitted that, although he felt sensuously satisfied with Goldie, something was lacking.

"It's the essential ingredient that's missing," I said. "Physical attraction is not enough. There is a loneliness in every human being which can only be filled by another with whom he or she can feel a complete union. It must encompass the mind as well as the body. I believe that this sort of union can only be achieved in marriage. Only a man and wife have the opportunity to develop that close companionship and understanding, that deep love in which giving is as important as receiving. When that exists, sexual love reaches the peak of perfection, because it is a consummation of this complete unity. It's worth working for, Bob."

"No argument about that as an ideal, Dr. Anchell," he agreed. "But how does a man work it out in real life?"

"You're lucky, Bob. If you really want to solve your problem, I feel sure you can. Patty wants to. After my conversations with both of you, I feel sure that you have a genuine, deep affection for each other. On a foundation like that, you can build a truly happy marriage.

"Sexually, you'll have to make an adjustment, a compromise," I stressed. "You have to accept the fact that you and your wife have different needs and desires as far as sex is concerned. You will have to indulge less often and she more often in the sex act than either of you actually wishes. Say three times a week instead of every night for you, and three times a week instead of none at all for her.

"You must realize, Bob, that Patty gets her greatest satisfaction from the affectionate aspect of love. Her enjoyment of intercourse depends to a great extent on her compassion for you, pleasing you, and your loving her completely. It is not necessary or possible for her to have an orgasm with each sex act as you do. As I explained to you before, your young wife hasn't yet experienced real orgasms. Once she does, and understands what it means to have a climax, she will learn to enjoy intercourse in a more physical sense and you will both find a richer fulfillment in the sensual expression of your love. Satisfactory orgasms, however, must be involuntary. Simulated ones such as Goldie has and as are taught to unsuspecting women by sex experts, are voluntary and fake.

"The mental attitude of both partners is the determining factor in a happy marital sex life. If you can convince Patty that you really love her for herself, then you'll realize how much she truly loves you. Your considering her as the most important person in the world to you will naturally remove her feminine reluctance."

Because they faced their problem honestly, with a mutual desire to solve it, Bob and Patty were able to work it out. It took determination and persistence to break the habits of quibbling and quarreling that had resulted from the fixed attitudes which had developed from the early maladjustment and misinformation. Bob learned to appreciate Patty's home-making skills as symbols of her love for him and also how to symbolize his love for her in the "silly little things" that mean so much to a woman—remembering birthdays and anniversaries, complimenting her on a new dress or hairdo, saying those three magic words, "I love you." Patty responded with warmth and affection. Their sex life became relaxed and pleasant. In a year or so, when Patty came of age sexually, theirs became the complete union that every couple seeks.

Unfortunately not every marriage reaches such a happy ending. The virus of confusion about sex matters has infected our entire modern society, and continues to spread its debilitating fever. The constant stream of misinformation that gushes from the motion-picture screen, the television tube, popular periodicals and novels—and from "official" books and advisers on sex as well—leads the average young husband to expect his bride to be as passionate as he and leads the average young wife to expect a gratification in the sex act which she does not find. As a result, many a marriage that could naturally develop into a rewarding partnership winds up as a divorce.

Even when the disillusioned partners learn the truth about the natural disparity in their sex drives, the marriage is not automatically salvaged. Knowledge of the disease does not necessarily guarantee its cure. The essential ingredient (discussed in Chapter 13) must be present. Seldom, if ever, is sensual attraction alone sufficient to hold a marriage together. Without the basis of affectionate love to build on, there is rarely enough incentive to make the necessary effort.

Even after a divorce, a young man or woman may stubbornly refuse to accept the truth. Doris, twenty-one and childless, was such a case. She and Sam had been drawn together by a strong physical attraction, which both misinterpreted as equal passion for genital sex. Their mutual disillusionment began soon after their honeymoon. Not understanding the cause of their incompatibility and having no other interests in common, they vented their pent-up resentments against each other and their unexpressed fears of personal impotence by constant bickering and quarreling.

One evening after a particularly heated argument, Doris left the house to seek solace in a neighborhood bar. She found it —she thought—in the attentions of the attractive man seated on the barstool next to hers. His compliments soothed her wounded ego. When, after a few more drinks, he suggested that they adjourn to a motel, it seemed like a good idea.

Afterward, however, Doris was more confused and disillusioned than before. This experience was even less satisfying than going to bed with Sam. In addition, she now had guilt feelings about her physical infidelity. To assuage these, as well as the gnawing doubt of her sexual capacity, she went to other motels with other men. Sam found out about it, and they wound up in the divorce court.

Doris came to see me sometime later because of a vaginal discharge which she feared was venereal disease. It proved to be an irritation of the vagina due to excessive douching. During the course of the tests her real problem came to light and we discussed it to a limited extent. Doris, however, did not want to face it realistically. She preferred to believe fiction rather than fact.

"You may be right about other women, Dr. Anchell, but it doesn't apply to me," she insisted. "What I need is a man whose sex drive is as strong as mine."

Doris is still searching for the right partner—and becoming an alcoholic in the process—because she keeps on trying to satisfy a false image of herself as a lustful wench, instead of her natural desires as a normal woman. She can only prove her importance as a woman and her value to men by being promiscuous.

From the complete adjustment of a couple like Patty and Bob to the complete maladjustment of a woman like Doris, there are varying degrees of adapting to nature's way. Contributing factors such as economic and social pressures, meddling in-laws and friends, illness, accident, or other outside influences may add to or accentuate marital difficulties. The average young couple, however, can usually meet such vicissitudes with courage and frequent success, if their marriage is founded on the two components of human sexuality—affectionate love and natural sex.

III

~~~~~~

The Middle of the Night

This chapter is titled in honor of Paddy Chayefsky's discerning drama *The Middle of the Night,* because the play so accurately portrays the dilemma of the average middle-aged man in regard to his sex life.

The hero is a lonely widower in his early fifties. In the middle of the night he is besieged by doubts and fears. He worries about losing his manhood. He feels panicked by the thought that life is passing him by.

When he meets the heroine, a young woman in her twenties, she is in the process of divorcing her young husband. Her problem is that of the average young wife who is repelled by the intensity of her husband's sex drive.

She is attracted by the older man, in whose company she feels relaxed and at ease. He finds her a delightful companion. They discover that they have many mutual interests, that the same values in life are important to them, that they prefer to be with each other more than with anyone else. Their friendship develops into a deep affectionate love, which is not without a warm physical attraction as well. They decide to marry.

At once an avalanche of objections descend upon them from all sides—family, friends, relatives, business associates. The two are of different religions and from different walks of life. The main theme of the objections, however, is the discrepancy in their ages. How can a woman in her twenties find sexual satisfaction with a man in his fifties?

The same doubts assail the couple, especially the man. They decide to find out before marriage. He is so afraid that he cannot satisfy her that his fears make him impotent. To his amazement, however, this does not upset his young fiancée. To her, the performance of the sex act is not essential. She loves him because of his love and appreciation of her as a person. He is so relieved by this discovery that he feels rejuvenated and becomes optimistic about regaining his virility. Both feel reassured that their marriage will be a success, because it is based on a love that is deeper than sexual desire.

Here the curtain falls on the stage drama. In real life, however, if the story were continued beyond this point, the roles in this couple's sex life would most likely be reversed. The decline in sexual activity in the average older man is primarily due to psychological rather than physical reasons. He is the victim of chronological confusion. He and the society he lives in are indoctrinated with the false idea that young women are so sexy that older men cannot satisfy them. The truth is exactly the opposite.

With the mental block removed, the middle-aged husband would regain his normal physical potency, and his young wife would probably be unable to satisfy him sexually. She might even have the same problem with him as she did with her young husband. The chances are, however, that the older man's superior finesse and understanding would make the sex act more pleasurable to her—as an intimate expression of their affectionate love instead of mere physical release.

As a general rule, an older lover is better able to please a young partner than the reverse. Experience makes him more sensitive to her needs and responses. Also, because of the popular opinion that he is second-best, he tries harder. In the case of the distinguished elder statesman, for example, whose marriages and divorces of young wives have been so widely publicized, I feel sure that it was not he who failed to satisfy his youthful brides, but vice versa.

As shown on the graph in Chapter 6 (see page 47), the average woman reaches the height of her sexual activity in her thirties and forties, although the intensity of her sex drive never equals that of the average man's at any age. During his thirties and forties, the average married man settles into regular sex habits, with the compliance of his wife. During this period much of the husband's energies are expended in making a living for a growing family and establishing himself in his field of work—whatever it may be, from unskilled labor to an exacting profession.

When the average man reaches his fifties, however, he usually has a resurgent desire for sex. His children are grown, and as an actual or potential grandfather he suddenly realizes that he is well into middle age. This is when he wakes up in the middle of the night haunted by phantom fears of lost manhood. To dispel these, there flames brightly within him a renewed interest in women and the genital sex act. He is attracted to younger women, subconsciously seeking the reassurance that if he can win their attention from young men, he must be "as good as he ever was."

To hold her husband through these dangerous years, the average wife must feign an interest in sex that she normally does not have. The average woman in her fifties is more concerned with companionate love. She may love her husband deeply, but feels less need to express her love sexually. Unfortunately the husband usually misinterprets his wife's natural indifference to the sex act as his own fault, due to his fancied inability to arouse her desire. Unless she understands and caters to his need for reassurance of his virility, he may endeavor to prove his prowess elsewhere. Fear of impotence drives him to an extramarital experiment. This is why many a chaste and faithful middle-aged husband suddenly becomes involved in a passionate love affair with a young woman.

Mr. N, a patient of mine, had been married twenty-eight

years and had three grown children, two of them married. He had started to work in his teens, and by diligent effort had developed a business of his own, which grew into a large manufacturing concern. Aside from his family, his sole interest had always been his work. Since he devoted many hours day and night to his business, his wife—a loyal and dutiful woman—had concentrated her attention and affection on the children. They continued to be of prime importance to her, even after they were grown.

In his early fifties, Mr. N became brooding and depressed. Although he continued to work diligently, he lost his heart for it. At this time he began to notice an attractive, twenty-three-year-old secretary in the office of one of the vice-presidents of his firm. As his interest grew, he started taking her to dinner after work, then going home with her to her apartment.

Suddenly one day Mr. N decided to sell his business and divorce his wife. With a burst of determination, he did both. Then he married the young secretary, and moved to another part of the country to live in retirement with his bride.

Popular sympathy, of course, was with his divorced wife. But unfair as it may seem, the burden of saving a marriage through this crucial period rests upon the wife. It is she who, in the middle of the night, must dispel her husband's self-doubts by expressing her love sexually. Their long years together should have deepened their affectionate love for each other, enriching the quality of their sexual love. And it is quality, not quantity, that a man needs at this crisis in his sex life. A mature wife is a better sex partner than any other average woman in her twenties.

When a man buries himself in his work, it is usually to compensate for a lack of companionship, affectionate and/or physical sexuality at home. The married woman who allows herself to become more a mother than a wife is courting loneliness in her later years. When her children are grown, they will leave her to live their own lives. If she has not remained her husband's partner, first and foremost, she may well lose him, too. If she does not let him know that she wants to be with him in the middle of the night, some other woman will.

In some societies, of course, this problem is handled by polygamy or prostitution. The middle-aged husband takes a new younger wife, a concubine, or a mistress. His older wife may remain his confidante and companion, or she may become an outcast. In reality, the end result is not so different from middle-aged extramarital affairs or divorces in our own society.

There is no right or wrong in regard to sexual relationships. They are either natural or unnatural. It is natural for a man to have a flare-up of sexual desire in his fifties—to need to prove that he is "still a man." If he is married, it is natural for him to want his wife to give him this reassurance. If she does not, it is not unusual for him to seek it outside of marriage. Fair or unfair to wives, it is the nature of things. A doctor can tell a man that he is sexually potent in his fifties, but in the middle of the night it takes a woman to prove it.

IV

~~~~~~~~~~~~~~~~~~~~~~~~~~~~~~~~~~~~

The Best Years of Your Life
—Grandparents

Grow old along with me!
The best is yet to be ...

In these lines of "Rabbi Ben Ezra" (named for a great
teacher who lived in the twelfth century), Robert Brown-
ing echoes the wisdom of eight centuries. Today, with such
a great increase in the average life span, the healthy older
person can look forward to many more of these best years
in which to savor the fullness of life. Yet modern man has
become so imbued with the cult of youth and action that he
finds it difficult to do so. Mr. A, one of my older patients, is
a typical example.

"Doctor, what am I going to do?" he asked me. "I don't
feel old! And I certainly know more than I did when I was
younger. Now I'm retired just because I'm sixty-five!" He
shifted his cuff to display the gold watch he'd received for
years of loyal service. "What am I supposed to do—sit and
listen to this thing tick the rest of my life away? What's the
fun of living on a pension? Why, I've worked for that com-

pany ever since I got out of school. I know my job but I don't know what to do with myself. I'll be lost."

"Work isn't the essence of life," I replied. "Just the pure enjoyment of living is a more permanent and rewarding occupation. Now you have time to be lazy—to look at the sky, to soak up the sunshine, to work in your garden and watch the miracle of growth. You have the chance to really appreciate being alive."

"What's the use of being alive and healthy, with nothing to do?" he argued.

"You might try getting acquainted again with Mrs. A," I suggested. "How long since you two have had time simply to sit down and enjoy each other's company? Or go for a walk? Or have a leisurely day doing nothing except being together? You say you don't feel old—why not try courting your wife again?"

Mr. A shook his head. "It sounds very romantic, Doctor. But she's the busy one these days—what with bridge and politics and one thing and another that she's got herself involved in."

"Why did she get involved in these activities?" I countered. "Because you were tied up in your work, and with the children grown and away from home, she had to have something to occupy her time and energy. I'm quite sure she would prefer just enjoying life with you. She's a vital and dynamic woman. You two should have a wonderful time together— a second honeymoon for the rest of your lives."

Mr. A sighed wistfully, but he was still unconvinced. He was so accustomed, mentally and physically, to the daily routine of work that it took him more than a year to readjust and wholeheartedly accept the fact that all he had to do was to relax and enjoy living. He was encouraged by his his wife, who willingly relinquished her outside activities.

Mrs. A had looked forward to the companionship of her husband's retirement. When he finally did "let go" and they entered this new phase of their life together, a beautiful glow of happiness erased the lines of strain and anxiety from her face. Mr. A confided that he was "happy as a bridegroom." "In fact," he added, "this second honeymoon is even better than the first. We're just as vigorous as when we were younger—but we've got a lot more in common than we did then."

As with the rest of nature, the autumn years of human life are intended to be those of fruition—of reaping the harvest for which the seed was planted and the soil tilled through the cares and responsibilities of raising a family. Unshackled from outside demands, married partners at this period of their lives can achieve the essence of human sexuality. Through the long years of sharing trials and triumphs, their affectionate love has ripened and may now find full richness of expression in the freedom of mature sexual love.

The sexual activities of youth fulfill nature's purpose for procreation, thus assuring reproduction of the species. But mature sex may be enjoyed as recreation, fulfilling the purpose of expressing love by the complete union of the partners.

For this reason menopause should be welcomed—not dreaded. Yet many a man and wife who have weathered the earlier, strenuous years successfully find their marriage teetering at this point, on the very threshold of the best years of their life together.

It is not only men who have "middle of the night" jitters, as discussed in the previous chapter. Women do, too. Although manifested in different ways, these anxieties in both sexes have their origin in primitive fertility worship—when survival of the human race depended upon producing as many offspring as possible. Today, however, the conquest of disease and other natural destroyers has reversed the problem. Mankind is now concerned with overpopulation. Yet the ancient taboos illogically and unrealistically persist in modern society and rise to haunt the middle-aged man and woman.

The woman who goes through an actual physical change at the time of menopause tends to have exaggerated fears about this perfectly natural process. She feels that she is withering on the vine of life. She worries about losing her femininity, becoming less attractive physically. It is not the prospective loss of sexual intercourse that troubles her primarily, but the loss of the inner security that comes from being needed and wanted. As a result she often tries to compensate by drawing attention to herself and arousing sympathy through an exaggeration of the minor physical discomfort that accompanies "change of life."

These simple physiological changes, which will be discussed in a later chapter (see Chapter 19), present no complications to a healthy female. Menopause is exactly what its name implies, an end of menstruation. No more, no less. It is not the end of the world, nor the end of life. It can be the beginning of a richer life.

A woman does not cease to be a woman when she ceases to menstruate. She does not change. She is the same person that she was before—just as attractive, intelligent, charming, and capable. The only difference is that she now has more freedom to express herself in every way, including sex. Not only is she free, at this age, from the responsibilities of childbearing and rearing, but she is also free from the necessity of using contraceptives. In reality, the "change of life" means her sexual emancipation.

The wife who becomes aware of this salient fact has little trouble holding her husband through the danger period, when he is having his own "menopausal" anxieties. As noted in the preceding chapter, this is when he worries about losing his virility and requires physical as well as mental reassurance. To the wife who fills this requirement, the husband naturally reciprocates with the assurance that she needs most at this time—affectionate understanding and companionship.

The wise husband shows his appreciation by remembering the little things that a woman treasures—not only anniversaries and birthdays, but special events that have a significance only to the two of them.

This is the wealth of the harvest years of marriage—the joy of being together, the sharing of small symbols that represent big moments, the awareness that the meaning of life is in life itself. This deeper sensitivity gives a quality and beauty to sexual love that is lacking in youth. Mature partners are better lovers than on their wedding night, because they have learned through self-control and consideration for each other how to attain the greatest pleasure in the sexual expression of their love. Added to this is the complete freedom that comes with the only natural contraceptive, the female menopause.

If a woman is childless, sometimes the finality of menopause brings on depression, because consciously or subconsciously she feels that she has not fulfilled nature's purpose. She need not despair. She can still become a mother by adopting a child. Adoption laws in most states have been broadened to make it possible for middle-aged couples and even single persons to become adoptive parents. The result is usually great happiness and fulfillment for both the child and the new parents.

The joy of having a child late in life is told by Maurice Goudeket in *The Delights of Growing Old.* A widower at seventy-one, the author married a woman about half his age. Her love and the birth of their son brought great enrichment to his life.

Statistics show that 70 percent of older married women enjoy sexual intercourse. In the unmarried category, due to the absence of a partner, only 12 percent indulge, but women in this group find other outlets for their energies and have more frequent sex dreams.

The so-called "male menopause" is mental, not physical. The male sex glands do not "dry up" as a man gets older, and such fears are completely unfounded. The testes keep right on manufacturing sperm, and the sperm keeps on wanting to be expelled. Although mental anxiety about impotence can produce temporary impotence, the function of the glands is not related to chronological age. In his recent studies of healthy human males of all ages, W. M. Johnson reports in *The Older Patient* that some of the oldest men had testicular activity equal to that of the youngest. The lessening of sexual activity among older men is not due to lack of capacity, but to the diversion of libidinal or sexual energies into other channels.

Mr. P, a patient of mine, was a vigorous old gentleman in his eighties when his wife died. He became very lonely. At a church social he met a widow in her early sixties whom he found quite congenial. She became fond of him, too, and they were married.

Soon afterward the now Mrs. P came to me in great distress. "The man is a sex maniac!" she declared. "Why, he wants intercourse all the time. An old man like that! Something terrible must be wrong with him."

"He's perfectly normal, Mrs. P," I assured her. "You two just haven't been married to each other long enough. It takes time, you know, to develop the close companionship that provides other outlets for showing affection. Be patient with him, give him love and understanding—and find other activities of mutual interest that will divert some of his energy."

"You mean I have to be a bride all over again, at my age?" she sighed. "Very well, I learned how to manage one husband and I can do it again."

The old adage "If youth but knew, and age but could" is only half true—the first half—as far as human sexuality is concerned. In the physical capacity for sex, age need make no bows to youth. And as for sex expertise—mother and father know best. So do grandmother and grandfather. Youth makes more sense sexwise by wanting to grow up than age does by wanting to cling to youth. Oldsters who feel compelled to compete with the "mad rush" of youngsters are

blind to their own blessings. They create needless frustrations
for themselves, which are exploited by hormone peddlers,
cosmetic manufacturers, and the like.

In my clinical experience with older patients, which is
considerable, I have found no justification for the rejuvenat-
ing claims made on behalf of sex hormones. The widespread
confidence in estrogen, the female hormone, as the elixir of
life for the woman over forty is, in my opinion, a delusion.
I have not seen any harmful effects following the use of
properly regulated estrogen for menopausal women. In my
own practice, however, I prescribed it only for certain
specific conditions in which it has shown definite therapeutic
value (see Chapter 19). As for male hormone treatment, the
ingestion or injection of such medicines apparently provides
a crutch that helps some men mentally. However, I seriously
question the physical value of such therapy.

Another mental roadblock that older people create to im-
pede their way to mature happiness is the preoccupation with
material values. Men, especially, tend to become so obsessed
with the striving for financial gain and its symbols of achievement, that they become frozen in a mental mold that equates
happiness with the accumulation of wealth and possessions.
When a man of this type becomes aware of advancing years,
panic seizes him at the prospect of losing his aggressive
capacity to compete with young men commercially and sexually. He feels that time is running out on him, and exhausts
himself in the effort to race against it. The resultant mental
fatigue and depression lessen his business acumen and his
sexual potency, thus giving credence to his fears. Preoccupied
with his own problems, and regarding his wife and his material provision for her primarily as status symbols, he neglects
to give her the personal attention and understanding which
she so desperately needs at this time. She in turn, feeling rejected, develops a resentment toward him. Both feel lonely and
unloved.

For solace, such people frequently turn to alcohol. It

gives a temporary relief by stimulating their lust fantasies—but results in further frustration when they try to act out their desires, because the physical effect of alcohol produces chemical impotence. This brings on additional fears of loss of sexualiy, leading to further resort to alcohol—and further impotence. The tragic cycle winds on, and the best years of life are squandered.

The accumulation of material things is no guarantee of happiness. Having them need not be a hindrance, but the essential ingredient of love must be paramount. Love of life in its natural simplicity, love of one's mate, love of one's fellow man. With this essential key to happiness in hand, a minimum of worldly goods will suffice.

A lack of basic material security, however, is a very real and distressing problem to many older people. Even in our enlightened society, with old age pensions provided by both private enterprise and government, there are still those who are in need of food, shelter, clothing, and health care. Small fixed incomes often become insufficient to meet the rising cost of living. Some, through circumstances or incapacity, have no income.

I believe that in our present society every older person can and should be provided with the basic necessities of life. If the individual wants to work, to supplement a pension or earn a living, and is capable of it, employment should be made available. Otherwise, his material needs should be provided for through social security laws. In spite of the fable of the ant and the grasshopper, I do not believe that the grasshopper should be left to starve. Even primitive societies take care of their elders and accord them a place of respect.

The natural requirements for happiness in one's later years are very simple: the assurance of material security and a loving mate. These are the only essentials for enjoying the pure pleasure of just living.

Some older people feel compelled to justify their existence by activity in intellectual, productive, or creative fields. If they are capable of such pursuits and find these necessary to their happiness, well and good. Personally and clinically, however, I feel that their compulsion will cause them to miss the real joy of life to which their later years entitle them.

Old age is the time when the human being can, at last, bask in his innate laziness without a troubled conscience. Throughout his life up to this point, the individual has been prodded like a pack mule to carry his load up and down the trail, day in and day out. Like despotic mule skinners, society and his own conscience have goaded him to work. He has been conditioned to believe that his inherent laziness—which is natural to every creature, including man— is bad, an evidence of worthlessness.

There is nothing wrong in the elemental desire to do nothing. Beneath all the man-made rationalizations, the basic motivation for work is the pleasure of relaxation that comes afterward. The end of the workday is the goal toward which the morning alarm clock summons us.

So it is with life. The autumn years signify the end of the long workday, when one can enjoy loafing with no guilt feelings whatsoever. This is the time to savor the essence of life, to rediscover with deeper awareness the pleasures of the senses—the sight of the sky and the earth and their myriad colors and forms; the sound of birdsong and rain and music; the smell of flowers; the taste of food; the warmth of the sun; and the touch of a loved companion.

The true values of life come into clearer focus with age. The older person who relaxes and enjoys them is doing what comes naturally.

> The joy of life is to live
> ————to see the stars.

V

~~~~~~~~~~~~~~~~~~~~~~~~~~~~~~~~~~~~~

Swingers

This typical ad from the classified section of a Los Angeles
daily newspaper indicates that in spite of all the brainwashing,
special inducements are still necessary to lure the female of
the human species into leading the unnatural sex life imposed
upon her by current customs. The more elaborate "passion
pads" and "sin bins" offer all sorts of recreational facilities and
programs, from Olympic-sized swimming pools to free hang-
over breakfasts on Sundays for these flourishing communities
of free lovers. All that the males need, of course, are the
females. The extras are designed to help overcome the females' natural reluctance, which persists in spite of two generations of false indoctrination.

Instinctively the female knows that her sex drive is not
of the same quality as the male's. But ever since women won
the right to vote in 1920, they have been trying to prove
themselves the equal replicas of men in every way. Their

instincts of mastery and self-determination, so long repressed
under male domination, have been asserted with a vengeance.
The Roaring Twenties toppled the double standard of sexual
behavior and proclaimed women's sexual emancipation. As
Frederick Lewis Allen reported of this period in *Only Yesterday:* "For the first time, the prostitute was faced with an
amateur competition of formidable proportions." The emancipated female has continued to confuse her instincts for
self-determination and independence with the instinct for
mating. This state of confusion has been aided and abetted
by the male, to whom such sexual freedom is a bonanza. It is
to his advantage to misinterpret Freud's libido principle, dis-
torting it to apply only to the physical sex act as a cure-all
for all tensions of both sexes. This false doctrine has been
perpetuated by an increasing hierarchy of sexperts. As a
result, the Swinging Seventies are in the midst of a free-love
binge that makes the petting parties of the Roaring Twenties
look like Sunday school picnics.

In the twenties, the open practice of free love in America
did not get beyond Judge Ben Lindsey's advocacy of companionate marriage, which caused a great deal of controversy.
Today, however, this sort of arrangement is commonly accepted by many colleges and universities. In a convenient off-
campus apartment, the coed couple sets up housekeeping for
the college term. The young lady expects that sex acts with
her boyfriend will strengthen his affectionate relationship
with her. However, when the male has sexual relations without having a sincere regard for his love object, his affection
and esteem are dissipated—not strengthened—by the sex act.
Frequently the same couple will remain together until graduation, then go their separate ways. The few marriages that do
occur in these circumstances are usually the result of the
young woman's insistence.

Such unstructured relationships—as the sexpert professors call them—are advantageous to the male student, who
normally develops sperm and prostatic secretions that need

to be physically elminated. Prior to student cohabitation such desires were disposed of by sublimating them into scholastic or other pursuits, by wet dreams, or perhaps by an occasional resort to a prostitute. It is much more convenient, of course, for him to have a coed roommate who is willing to be used as a receptacle for the natural accumulations of his sex organs. Such a relationship, however, can hardly be conducive to mutual love and respect.

According to a recent survey (*Newsweek*, July 4, 1966), the chief factor in these student free-love arrangements is the birth control pill, whose use "demonstrates that a girl can behave like a boy." The fallacy is that a girl does not *naturally* behave like a boy. Removal of the fear of pregnancy is *not* the touchstone unleashing the female erotic nature.

Unlike the average human male, the average female does not reach zeniths of ecstasy during each sex act. In fact, she may not find sensual pleasure in many experiences. It is therefore essential that she be in love with her mate, so that the lack of physical satisfaction may be offset by the satisfaction of pleasing the man she loves. Love, for a woman, means a relationship that gives her assurance that her man holds her in the highest regard, enjoys her companionship, likes to make her happy. When she is loved in this way, the woman responds by giving herself as a companion and as a physical being.

The misguided female who tries to conform to the male standard of physical sex is doomed to bitter disillusionment. To hide her disappointment and feeling of inadequacy, she may "mouth" expressions of pleasure concerning her sex experiences and thus delude others of her own sex into making the same mistake. She also deludes herself by continued experimentation in the vain hope that she may finally achieve the anticipated sexual satisfaction. Since her conscious mind refuses to accept the futility of her situation, her subconscious seeks devious means of releasing its built-up tensions. Some women, prone to obsessiveness about total independence from men, strengthen their intellects and become excellent incomplete men. In their efforts to acquire equality, their female emotionality becomes dry and sterile through intellectual suppression. These women usually demand to have erotic experiences without the normal feminine pre-requisite of love or longing for love. They desire only to get rid of sexual tensions under conditions that commonly charac-terize the man. Misleading these women into trying to parallel men in erotica, some contemporary sexperts are providing instructions teaching these women to have artificial orgasms. Instead of waiting for definite conditions to be fulfilled that allow the vaginal muscles to contract spontaneously, the females learn to contract their vaginas voluntarily and on cue with the male orgasm. These simulated orgastic responses are used as proof by the sexperts that woman's biological differ-ences are due to social influences and not to constitutional factors.

For example, Mrs. S, a young divorcée, came to me com-plaining of headaches and overweight. She was a very attrac-tive and intelligent businesswoman, not at all the kind who develop illnesses out of boredom. However, except for her weight problem, I could find nothing physically wrong with her. I felt sure that the source of her difficulty was psychosomatic and that it would reveal itself in due course. In the meantime, I put her on a diet, the only one I know that is permanently effective for losing weight. (Melvin Anchell, M.D.: *How I Lost 36,000 Pounds.*)

At first Mrs. S followed the diet faithfully. As it took effect, however, and her figure became more attractive, she stopped dieting, gained several pounds, and again complained of headaches.

By this time a closer rapport had developed, and my patient's real problem began to come into the open. Mrs. S was unable to correlate her lack of interest in sex with the attitude expected of her by her social group. She admitted that she was a "real swinger," who believed in indulging in the sex act whenever one felt the urge, and that "the boys" could always count on her to cooperate. But, she confessed, she actually got no satisfaction out of it, and indulged only because it was "being done," and because she wanted to feel wanted.

"I can't understand why I don't enjoy it," Mrs. S said in a worried voice. "My girl friends tell me how they really get with it, and even cry out in ecstasy. Of course," she added, "I don't dare admit to them that I don't get the same kick out of the sex act that they do—so I tell them that I react the same way. I wish I did! Why don't I?"

"You don't, because your reaction is perfectly natural and normal," I assured her. "And if your girl friends told the truth, I'm sure they would admit that they feel exactly as you do. The primitive woman, yielding to her sexual desires without conflict, is found only in fiction. In reality the harmonious feminine woman cannot express herself with too great a sexual freedom, for it results in mental confusion. There must be a harmonious interplay of feminine psychological forces with the art of sexual love."

"You mean it's not abnormal for a woman to dislike sexual intercourse?" Mrs. S asked in surprise. "I thought women were supposed to have the same sex drive as men. That's what all these sex books say."

"Unfortunately, the greatest number of sex books and the most popular are by male self-styled experts who have had no clinical medical experience," I explained. "They don't know what they're talking about. They have pet theories, which are actually nothing but male wish fulfillments dressed up in impressive terminology. In real life, it just isn't so."

"It certainly isn't so in my case," Mrs. S. agreed. She said that she had entered into her early sex experiences with a great deal of zest, anticipating that she would find reality to equal her fantasies. When these rewards did not materialize, she developed fears of being "different and abnormal." Mrs. S, a capable, well-paid business executive, decided to become pregnant "to bring out her latent womanhood." Her bachelor motherhood, however, failed to develop these feelings; instead her disgust with free love and motherliness became complete.

Finally she tried marriage. The marriage, however, did not last. Now divorced, Mrs. S has turned to building a business career and supporting her child.

As our discussions progressed, it became clear that Mrs. S's compulsive eating was a subconscious defense mechanism to keep her from being attractive to men, so that she would not have to go to bed with them and prove herself a woman. She admitted that she had tried dieting several times previously—with the same result. As soon as she began to look "sexy" and handsome men started asking her for dates, her tension headaches came on and she ate like a glutton.

When Mrs. S realized that her attitude toward sex was the natural one for an average woman, her feelings of inadequacy were so relieved that she was able to reduce her weight to a pleasingly plump stage and hold it there. She is now much more comfortable both physically and mentally, although the scars of her previous traumatic experiences will never be entirely erased.

Men, too, are subject to psychological trauma in connection with their sex life. Although the human male has a physical need for the sex act, it is never completely satisfying to him without love. He also craves affection, companionship, and understanding—a mate to whom he is the most important person in the world and who wants to make him happy. Simply having sexual intercourse is not enough. He will pick up an accommodating female and go to bed with her for physical relief, but this partial satisfaction will not make him want to stay with her or return to her. He keeps on seeking other women, hoping to find the "right one" who will satisfy his longings for a more intense, complete fulfillment. When his search continues to be unrequited, he feels cheated. Women satisfy his lust but not his love. His unfulfilled longings for affection and companionship frequently become distorted into hate for all women, and he becomes a sadist in his sex life.

Dr. F is that kind of man. Now in his forties, he has been through five marriages and five divorces, as well as innumerable affairs. He is a surgeon—not a good one from the point of view of colleagues who assist at his operations—but in the eyes of his patients he is a god. He has a high position on the hospital staff. His passion in surgery is for hysterectomies (removal of the female reproductive organs).

Dr. F looks like a model for the Man of Distinction—handsome, charming, with a regal bearing that makes most people, men as well as women, automatically defer to him. Life has always been easy for him—too easy. Women have been especially easy for him. Since he was an adolescent, he has been able to have any female he wanted. Yet he has never known love. It has been impossible for him to give or receive affection, so his prolific sex life has been a continuous succession of frustrations. His bitterness and disappointment with sensual sexuality devoid of the affectionate component have built up such a reservoir of hate for women that his sadism is almost fiendish.

He continues to ejaculate his sperm into female vaginas, but his real release comes when he destroys his hapless partners—not openly, of course. With subtle scorn, contemptuous and contemptible humor, he tears them apart in conversations with his friends—and theirs. When he finishes with a woman, she is a social outcast.

In surgery, he literally tears women apart. I have never seen such butchery. Yet after he sews his patients up and comes to their bedside in his suave and courtly manner, they thank him tearfully for saving their lives.

How any nurse who has seen Dr. F operate can become personally intimate with him is more than I can understand. Yet he attracts them as raw meat attracts flies. Then he takes malicious delight in having them fired from their jobs. Again, not openly. In the same manner as he destroys other women socially, he destroys the luckless nurses professionally. When the unknowing victim comes to bid him good-bye, he sympathizes and wishes her godspeed. He is always careful to inquire where she is going to apply for another job and makes sure that his personal "recommendation" gets there first. His sadism has spilled inwardly into himself and he is gradually destroying his life with an increased use of alcohol and by turning to perverted sexual relations with men. Additional satisfaction comes from his control over these men, so that he gets whatever he wants—at the hospital, at the club, wherever he goes.

This is not an extreme case. "Free love" debases two of the noblest words and emotions of mankind, and the degradation is infectious. It is a psychological venereal disease that destroys people and civilizations.

There is nothing new in the doctrine of free love and its attendant perversions. It has been tried before, time and time again throughout history—always with the same old argument that sexual promiscuity and perversion are "natural"—and always with the same result, the suicide of a civilization.

Free love is self-destructive because it is unnatural. Nature made the male sex drive much more intense than the female's for a very good reason. It is an old truth that has not changed from prehistoric times that man's sexual desires are intensified if he has to overcome obstacles before achieving sexual communion with women, and that women are more completely gratified with sexual intimacy only after a long wooing. Opposition heightens the intensity of any instinct. When the male receives stimulating opposition to his mating urge, he will then use his excess libidinal energies to create a more favorable situation. However, if mating is achieved without effort on the part of the male, all his libidinal energies become dissipated in the sex act. If it continues to be too easy, the mating instinct itself deteriorates into impotence. All the male's creative energies die out, and so does the species.

As discussed in Chapter 7, the whole progress of human civilization depends upon the male's being thwarted to a natural extent in his mating instinct. When the female plays hard to get she is aiding this process. She is fulfilling the role in which nature cast her, and mankind progresses. When she goes against nature and becomes a "free lover," the female destroys not only herself but the future of the civilization of which she is a vital part. Contrary to nature, pornographers and the sexperts depict the woman as a rapist.

VI

∼∽∼∽∼∽∼∽∼∽∼∽∼∽∼∽∼∽∼∽∼∽∼∽

Clinical Sexual Truths

Medical truths, whether related to human sexuality or physical problems, spring from observations, not from established
social opinions or decadent dogmas. All knowledge is a result
of man's observing his environment. A physicist studying
universal laws, a chemist learning the composition of matter,
or anyone seeking an understanding of nature determines the
fact this way. Medical science, especially, is dependent on the
everyday medical observations of the practicing physician.

Academic works regarding human sexuality may be conducted in the peculiar setting we call the psychiatric hospital,
but, these "test-tube" studies are valueless unless they can be
substantiated by the acid test of the day-to-day world of the
practicing physician treating the "whole patient."

Today, the trend for evaluating medical and social truths is
just the opposite. The public has been indoctrinated to place
tremendous weight, often in excess of their importance, on the
personal findings of affluent academicians who have no real
clinical experience. This popular entrancement with the
opinions of such authorities is best described by a phrase
coined by Dr. Karl Menninger, the dean of American psychiatry, "antiquated scholasticism." The worship is based on
the principle that what is important depends on "who says
what, rather than what is said."

In an address before 170 judges of the fifth annual Wisconsin Judicial Conference, Dr. Menninger cautioned against our nation's reliance on "antiquated scholasticism." There is no basis for it, he said. "I have absolutely no use for such a finding."

A primary source of information for the institutional professors is the statistical laboratory. In studying emotional problems, the statisticians select questions separated from the complete mental situation. The artificially acquired information is, quite frequently, contrary to clinical findings.

The statistical-questionnaire-control-group method is extremely inaccurate for studying human behavior; there is no substitute for clinical examination of actual cases. Freud recognized this fact when he said that the physician must return to observing his patients to learn truth.

Psychiatrist Samuel A. Nigro, in an article published by the *Journal of the American Medical Association* (November 30, 1970), says:

My own experience suggests that any answer [to medical and psychological truths] must include the fact that the Art of medicine cannot be formulated until psychiatrists become directly familiar with the problems of medical practice . . . the one-to-one must be made teachable to enable physicians to meet psychological needs. Both patients and physicians will suffer until this is done.

Freud's genius lay in understanding the whole of human nature, in discovering the human mental apparatus which controls the delicate balance between life and death. No one has equaled Freud in an in-depth study of human sexuality. Certain of Freud's principles, as they have been applied in my own clinical experience, will be discussed in later chapters.

Enlightening research on the sexual behavior of humans has been the more recent contribution of Alfred C. Kinsey. It was my good fortune to have studied under him at the Neuropsychiatric Institute of Columbia University in

1945, while I was in the Army Medical Corps. At that time, Kinsey was compiling and analyzing the statistics which formed the basis of his now famous reports on the sexual behavior of both men and women (*Sexual Behavior in the Human Male*). Though most of his material sounded quite revolutionary in those days, I was impressed with the thoroughness and precision of his particular statistical research. It was qualitative as well as quantitative, like a meticulous experiment in a chemical laboratory. The investigative questionnaire that Kinsey used to compile his statistical data produced extraordinarily accurate information. All possible variables were taken into consideration. It was with a great deal of interest that I later put Kinsey's report to the acid test of clinical observations.

My experience throughout the years with both male and female patients, and especially female, verifies the soundness of the general findings of Freud and Kinsey.

Clinical Findings

The accompanying graph shows the natural patterns of sexual behavior in men and women from ages thirteen to sixty-three, according to my own records. With only slight variations, this clinical report tallies with the results of Kinsey's statistical research.

It is based on the number of orgasms—climaxes of the sex act—which the average human male or female is capable of having per week. It is to be regarded in the same manner as tables of average heights and weights, *i.e.*, not every person precisely fits into the average pattern. The reader's sex drive may be more or less intense than that shown on the graph. What is normal for one person is not necessarily normal for his neighbor or even for his brother or sister. Within moderate variations, however, I have found that the general patterns shown here apply to about 75 percent of my patients.

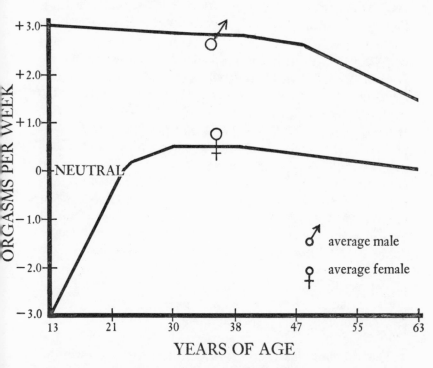

Chart shows intensity of drive in men and women for sexual intercourse as measured by number of orgasms the average *male and female are capable of having per week. Minus sign indicates degree of aversion to genital sex.*

This actual clinical record of "doing what comes naturally" contradicts certain popular misconceptions—especially in regard to the natural sex drives of men and women and the sexual capacities of young and older age groups.

THE MALE:

As the graph shows, the *average* human male between the ages of thirteen and thirty is capable of three orgasms per week, with a very gradual decline over the next twenty-five years to two per week at age fifty-five, and a slight decrease thereafter to an average of three every two weeks at age sixty-three. Over a span of fifty years, the male sex drive decreases only by half. The sixty-three-year-old grandfather cannot be ruled out as a rival to his thirteen-year-old grandson.

This does not mean that the average boy of thirteen actually indulges three times a week—or at all—in the sex act. Although he is perfectly capable of it, his natural physical urge is usually restrained by his ego and his conscience and is redirected into other channels.

When the restraints are lifted, or he throws them off, the young unmarried man often feels that he must have sexual intercourse whenever and wherever it is available. He may have as many as fifteen or more climatic sex acts in a single week as insurance against empty weeks when no female partner is available.

The married man usually settles into regular sex habits, averaging three times per week—sometimes more, sometimes less, depending upon the circumstances.

With advancing years, the male's sex drive gradually lessens in intensity—not necessarily because of any decrease in the ability to perform the sex act, but because other satisfactory outlets for physical and mental energies have been developed.

THE FEMALE:

With few exceptions, the *average* woman does not have a genuine orgasm before age twenty-five or twenty-six.

As the graph demonstrates, the *average* female of thirteen has a complete aversion to sexual intercourse. She wants no part of it. She likes to be petted or indulge in other sensual but not genital sex acts. That's as far as she wants to go.

By her early twenties, the young woman has attained a passive or neutral attitude, a willingness to participate in genital sex in order to please the man she loves.

At age twenty-five or twenty-six, the average woman experiences her first real orgasm. This is when she usually falls in love physically with her sex partner.

By age thirty, she usually reaches her maximum of two orgasms *per month*—not per week. One climax generally occurs just before or just after menstruation, and one when the ovum, or egg, is expelled. Since the average woman of thirty to forty is married and her sex life is adjusted to her husband's needs, she may feel that her sexual activity is more intense than the graph shows. True, she may participate more often and find sensual pleasure with her husband. For her, however, the sex act is seldom climactic more than twice monthly.

After forty, when her menstrual periods start to become irregular and menopause ensues, the average woman gradually returns to a neutral or passive attitude—but with a difference. The sixty-three-year-old grandmother not only has a greater physical capacity for sex than her thirteen-year-old granddaughter, she is also—unless she has become prey to false fears—better adjusted to it psychologically than the average twenty-year-old.

The misinformation that in youth the mating urge of male and female is equally intense has been perpetuated both by old-fashioned romanticists who sing of love in the spring, and by modern pseudo realists who rationalize in scientific terminology. All such sexual interpretations are based on common sense, which is often nonsense. In reality, the contrast between the male and female sex drives is most marked in the young. The lustful fantasies of boys and young men center on genital sex. The romantic dreams of girls and young women involve kisses and caresses and tender words of love, and often embody the desire to bear a child—but seldom, if ever, include the actual sex act necessary for conception. These findings apply to people in all walks of life, with varied backgrounds and teachings. It is not due to artificial inhibitions devised by society. It is simply the nature of things as they are—not as the male wishes them to be.

Men and women are most nearly matched in their sex drives during their thirties and forties. Even then, the male urge is far more intense, but the female partner can understand it better because she, too, experiences a climax from time to time. As the partners grow older, mutual understanding of each other's needs usually deepens and so does their affectionate love. Thus mature couples should, and generally do, have a more satisfactory sex life than they did during the early years of their marriage.

VII

~~~~~~~~~~~~~~~~~~~~~~~~~~~~~~~~~~~

The Sexperts

The new hierarchy of sexperts, which has developed since the 1920s, has given a false aura of scientific sanction to the cult of free love. In spite of Freud's specific warning against such a dangerous misconception, his discoveries regarding human sexuality have been misinterpreted and distorted to justify the male lustful wish fulfillment. Freud's original principles, formulated on the basis of thorough and painstaking clinical research, concern the psychological aspects of human sexuality. Nowhere does he advocate the physical sex act, as such, as a prescription for relief of tension. In fact, he warns against the dangers of such misguided practice.

The sexperts contend that the physical sex act comprises the whole of human sexuality and that it is a strictly automatic bodily function in the same category as breathing, eating, sleeping, sweating, digesting food, and eliminating waste. The female's natural disinclination for sexual intercourse is attributed to the inhibitions of hypocritical social, cultural, and religious standards.

According to the sexperts, the moral code is not a natural one. They concede—in fact, they teach—the evolution of life in all other respects. But for reasons of their own, they deny this natural process in regard to sexuality and arbitrarily place human sexual relationships in the same classification as those of unicellular organisms

Therefore, they say, humans should be as promiscuous as amoebas, for if they are not allowed this free-wheeling sex life, they will tend to develop tensions and neuroses for which the cure-all is free-love relationships.

The sexperts do admit an anatomical difference between the human and the amoeba. To overcome this disadvantage, they recommend physical erotic stimulation of the female to break down her resistance to having indiscriminate sexual relations. This concept has been disseminated to young people, who refer to it as "getting the girl turned on."

Victims of this disastrous hoax frequently come to the physician seeking a cure for physical ills, most of which prove to be psychosomatic. I have had many such patients, including members of sexperts' families.

Although he denounces the rigidity of society's established codes, the sexpert is adamant in adhering to and enforcing his own. He has brainwashed himself as well as his followers.

Sybil's father, for example, is a sexpert—a clinical psychologist highly regarded by his patients and his professional colleagues. Although he and his wife have made a concession to social conventions by living as a chaste married couple, they otherwise try in every way to practice what he preaches about sex, including indoctrinating his daughter in the philosophy of "free love." Accordingly, when Sybil started menstruating at age thirteen, her father equated her sex needs with those of the average thirteen-year-old boy. He instructed his daughter thoroughly in the tenets of his code, including the use of contraceptives.

Being a perfectly normal thirteen-year-old girl, Sybil was not interested in the genital sex act beyond a natural mental curiosity. This was more than satisfied by her father's exposition. Accepting his teachings implicitly, she was disturbed because she felt none of the desire for mating which he told her was so natural.

She was quite attractive and her parents belonged to the country club set, many of whom came to her father for counseling. In accordance with the custom of her social group, Sybil started dating when she was fourteen. Although she enjoyed dancing and petting, she was still not interested in the sex act. Because of her father's indoctrination, however, she felt obligated to gratify the physical needs of her boyfriends. The word got around, and Sybil became very popular. She also became very unhappy.

It was not her conscience that troubled her. She accepted the sex act with the same moral indifference as she did breathing, eating, sleeping, as her father had taught her. But he had also promised that this attitude would insure the continuance of the happy, healthy, well-adjusted outlook on life that she had enjoyed in childhood. It didn't. It had exactly the opposite effect; her normal adolescent feminine need to sublimate eroticism and to engage in platonic love was destroyed by engaging in sexual activity. She reacted with feelings of emptiness and disappointment. Sybil felt sure this must be due to some inadequacy in herself. She was ashamed to bring her problem to her parents, because she felt that she had failed them in not being ecstatically happy with genital sex relations. Not questioning their wisdom, she kept on trying to please them and to find the promised release for her own tensions by continuing her promiscuous sexual activities—the antidote her father prescribed for all emotional problems.

She began to find release when, at sixteen, her parents invited her to join them in the cocktail hour before dinner. Alcohol, Sybil discovered, bolstered her feelings of confidence in her own femininity. This reassurance could be sustained even during sexual intercourse, if she had enough drinks. By the time she entered college, Sybil was holding her liquor very well. Her popularity among the more sophisticated, uninhibited male students led to increased sexual activity, and with it an ever-increasing need for alcoholic stimulation. She became sexually and alcoholically saturated.

At twenty-three, Sybil is a confirmed alcoholic. Her parents

are aware that somewhere aong the line they made an error
in her training. But to the sexpert, his credo is inviolate.
He is more bigoted than the Puritan or Victorian whom he
denounces. Sybil's father has a completely blocked mind
when it comes to relating his daughter's alcoholism to her
unnatural sex life.

Girls who are promiscuous and who do not abide by
feminine inhibitions toward eroticism fail to draw sexual
strength from the feminine psyche. Later in life they are
unable to fuse their sexual longings with their longings for
ideal love satisfactorily. They live their lives seeking erotic
love and the grand passion, even after they are married.

When the life instincts are perverted, the death instincts
take over. This is one of nature's inexorable laws. The first
step toward self-destruction is an unnatural sexual adjustment.
The alarming increase in alcoholism, drug addiction, and
suicide in our society today can be attributed to this basic,
underlying cause. LSD, marijuana, and "goof balls" are
popular adjuncts to the uninhibited sex lives of many of our
young people.

The sexperts are bringing disaster not only upon themselves but upon countless innocent victims. This is the
tragedy that Freud tried to forestall when he issued his
warning against "wild psychoanalysis" (*The Complete
Psychological Works*, Vol. XI) in 1910. In this paper
Freud severely criticized doctors who even then were advising their patients that anxiety states were due to the lack
of physical sexual release, and furthermore were falsely
attributing this "new discovery" to Freud himself.

Citing the case of a physician who had advised a woman
patient to relieve her mental anxieties by engaging in sexual
intercourse or masturbation, Freud said:

I may do a man who is unknown to me [the physician] an injustice by connecting my remarks about wild Psycho-analysis
with this incident. But by so doing I may perhaps prevent others
from doing harm to their patients. . .

The physician was ignorant of a number of scientific theories of psycho-analysis or had misapprehended them. . . . The doctor's advice to the lady shows clearly in what sense he understands the expression "sexual life"—namely, in which by sexual needs nothing is meant but the need for coitus or analogous acts producing orgasm and emission of the sexual substances. . . .

In psycho-analysis the concept of what is sexual comprises far more. . . . We reckon as belonging to "sexual life" all the activities of the tender feelings . . . even those impulses which have exchanged their sexual aim for another which is no longer sexual. . . .

The mental in sexual life should not be overlooked or underestimated. We use the word "sexuality" in a comprehensive sense. . . . We have long known that mental absence of satisfaction with all its consequences can exist where there is no lack of normal sexual intercourse.

Anyone not sharing this view of sexuality has no right to adduce psychoanalytic theses dealing with the etiological (causative and curative) importance of the sex act.

By emphasizing exclusively the somatic [physical] factor in sexuality he undoubtedly simplified the problem greatly . . . but he alone must bear the responsibility for what he does. . . .

No one can ever believe that sexual satisfaction in itself constituted a remedy for the suffering of neurotics.

In that last statement, Dr. Freud was overly optimistic about the integrity or the intelligence of a vast number who claim to have knowledge of the science of psychiatry which he founded. The sexperts do believe that the sex act in itself is a cure-all.

Could the sexperts be right? Could Freud—and nature itself—be wrong?

The sexperts say that human sexuality is an automatic bodily function, just like breathing. One breathes alone. One can eat alone. One can sleep alone (some even prefer it). One can sweat without assistance. One digests food in his own stomach. One can go to the toilet by himself.

But the sex act takes two. Masturbation is not sexual

intercourse. Therefore sex differs from breathing, eating, etc., which would seem to invalidate the first point in the sexpert's credo.

But suppose the sexperts are correct in their other concepts? Suppose that men and women do have equally strong sex drives, that free love is the natural method of satisfying both, and that the sex act should be unrestricted. How would this apply in modern human civilization? A Day in the Life of Mr. X would go like this:

Mr. X, having just completed an after-breakfast sex act with his wife, zips up his pants, grabs his briefcase, and starts off to the bus stop. As he passes a neighboring house, Mrs. Neighbor comes out to take in the milk from the doorstep. When she and Mr. X say good morning to each other, the urge seizes them. Mr. X puts down his briefcase, Mrs. Neighbor puts down her milk bottles, and they both lie down on the grass. That attended to, Mr. X hurries on to the bus stop, where an attractive young lady is sitting on the bench. She looks at Mr. X, he looks at her, and before the bus arrives they have sexual intercourse.

On the bus Mr. X turns his attention to the papers in his briefcase, and so arrives at his office without further incident. His competent secretary, who awakened early that morning from a sexual dream about her employer, wastes no time in making the dream come true. They are both so stimulated that very little work gets done that morning. Mr. X goes to lunch at his favorite bistro. With his first martini, he and the topless barmaid get the same reflex at the same time, and other customers wait while she and Mr. X attend to their physical needs.

Need I go on?

Nature is not imperfect, there is a reason for whatever *it* does. If women had the same sex drives as men, all other human activities would cease to a large degree in deference to the mating instinct—*for a while*—then all activities would cease, even the mating instinct. Instincts need opposition to survive. These energies have formed to overcome forces in the environment opposing their urge. If we want to see how such instincts are destroyed, we have only to look at the gorilla today.

The gorilla, the animal most closely resembling man, is a dying species, not because of leopards and hunters, but because he now lives in the ideal state of existence advocated by the free-love sexperts. Contrary to horror movies and other fiction, the male gorilla is not aggressive sexually or otherwise. Native Africans call him "the lazy black man of the jungle." He may have been fierce once, when females were hard to find. But mating has been so easy for so long that he has become practically impotent. When the female gorilla is in heat, she has to rub and play with the male's genitals for a long time to stimulate him to action, and she does not always succeed in arousing him. If there is no mating there are no baby gorillas to perpetuate the species.

Even some of the sexperts are now admitting that free love is not the answer. Perhaps they realize that because many females may not take their birth control pills, the population explosion could reach the proportion of the experimental rat cage which became so crowded that the rats began eating one another.

Now following their prototypes in long dead ancient civilizations, the more advanced sexperts are advocating more obvious perversions than free love. Perhaps, so they theorize, homosexuality, bestiality and oral copulation are really the most nautral relationships for humans. It would, indeed, solve the population problem—just as it did in Babylon and Rome.

VIII

~~~~~~~~~~~~~~~~~~~~~~~~~~~~~~~~~~~

First Love

Parents wonder why the streams are bitter, when they themselves have poisoned the fountain.

—Locke

No matter whom you "sing along with"—a TV personality, a group on a camping trip, or around the family piano—inevitably you came to that old favorite:

> I want a girl
> Just like the girl
> Who married dear old Dad!

It is more than tunefulness that accounts for the perennial popularity of this song. It expresses a basic wish of every normal male. The songwriter who composes a companion piece for the girls who want to "marry a man just like dear old Dad" will have another hit that outlasts the fads.

It is perfectly natural for a child to say, "When I grow up, I'm going to marry Mommy"—or Daddy—as the case may be. And subconsciously that is exactly what happens. That there should be a love between the child and parent throughout life is generally acknowledged as a normal relationship. However, when ordinary day-to-day observations and analysis of patients reveal that children have a sensuous love for the parent, as well as compassionate love, the idea is horrifying to most minds. The reaction is as it should be. From the earliest of times, man has had a dread of incest and the fear has been deeply ingrained in his descendants. Though the child's wish to express sensual feelings for a love object who provides for all his needs is not unrealistic, the parent is not an appropriate object for this type of love. Incestuous feelings arouse an inherent guilt in the minds of children. The guilt is further supported by the attitudes of family and society toward these urges. The child learns to suppress and redirect his sensual feelings for the parent. The way in which he converts these drives largely determines his later sexual adjustment.

The early years of a child's life set the basic patterns for all later behavior. Sexual adjustment, especially, begins at birth.

The unborn infant in the womb exists in a state of Freudian pleasure—relieved of all excitation and stimulation, the instinctual energies quiescent. The temperature and environment of the uterus are as nearly ideal as is physically possible. Food and oxygen are supplied through the umbilical cord. If the mother in some way causes a disturbance of this idyllic existence, the fetus responds with a kick of protest. At the time of delivery, when the uterus is contracting and pressing against the baby's body, tiny arms and legs flail out in an attempt to fight off these undesirable effects disturbing his peace. When the infant emerges into the colder air of the external world and must use his own lungs to survive, he cries out lustily against this hostile environment. A like response greets the doctor's spank.

This newborn human being is now on his own and must allow the instinctual energies, by which the race has survived, to come forth and help him survive. Utterly dependent, his first instinct is to seek the source of warmth and food —his mother. Matching the child's need for an outside love object interested in maintaining its life, nature has endowed the mother with a motherly instinct. The touch of her body soothes the infant, and the milk from her breast appeases his hunger. She gratifies his every need outside her body, just as she did inside. Once more tranquil, he sinks into the bliss of sleep, devoid of all care.

In fulfilling her duties and love for the child, the parent's innumerable activities for the infant awaken the child's sexual instincts. Bathing, playing, and caressing the child are ways in which sensual feeling is awakened in the child, helping him to grow. His first satisfactions are tactile (touch) and oral (mouth). The first source of these pleasures is from his mother. As she tends to his creature comforts, caresses and fondles him, he feels the flow of her protective love, and he responds in kind. In infancy, the child's love for the mother is all-encompassing. He desires to possess her completely.*

The child's first intellectual curiosity is in the discovery of various parts of his own body and the anatomy of others.

To girl as well as boy babies, the mother is the first love object outside themselves. She is not only the source of pleasure, but of sustenance, safety, and comfort. This memory and feeling persists subconsciously throughout life. I have seen many an older patient who has suffered a stroke or other illness or injury to the brain, and who during the semiconscious state—temporary or permanent—calls out for "Mama! Mama!" just as a frightened child lost in a strange world.

After the differences between the sexes are discovered, the father normally becomes the principal love object of the little girl, while the mother remains the little boy's love object.

* Mothers are sometimes troubled by what they feel are "guilty thoughts" of a sexual nature while they are tending to the physical needs of boy babies, such as diapering or bathing or teaching them to use the toilet. Such thoughts are perfectly natural responses to anatomy. The fact that the conscious mind recognizes and supresses them so that they are not acted upon is a sign that they are nothing to worry about. Thoughts are not actions, and they can be dismissed without consequence or feelings of guilt.

This initial love of the child for the parent of the opposite sex is subconsciously entwined with the instinctual desire for pleasure through sensual activities. As the baby grows from infancy to childhood, the little boy wishes in some way to involve the mother in arousing the pleasurable excitations associated with his genitals and the little girl fantasizes having a child of the father. Because such activities are limited to relationships between the parents, the boy simultaneously respects and resents his father. The girl has similar feelings toward her mother, but her resentment is usually not so strong, because it is tempered by the original love that existed between the mother and daughter at birth.

These feelings are seldom openly expressed but find release in dreams and games. A boy's games are more aggressive and hostile, because of the subconscious wish to eliminate the male rival (the father) and rescue the fair maiden (the mother) so he can have her all to himself. Since the little girl subconsciously wishes only to replace her mother, not eliminate her, girls' games are imitative, not aggressive. While her brother prefers toy guns, swords, bats, and balls, the girl mimics her mother by playing with baby dolls, toy bake sets, and stoves, acting out the role of a wife and mother. In the subconscious sexual rivalry for the loved parent's attention, the little boy may imitate his father's actions and mannerisms to impress his mother, and the little girl will dress up in her mother's clothes to attract her father.

This early sexual attraction between a boy and his mother is called the Oedipus complex—so named by Freud from the ancient Greek myth dramatized in the *Oedipus Rex* by Sophocles. The same attraction between a girl and her father is called an Electra complex. The timeless appeal of this drama is attributed to the fact that it enacts the fulfillment of the childhood lust wish for the parent and the subconscious guilt feelings that normally follow.

The play concerns the fate of Oedipus, the son of royal parents, who as an infant was abandoned to die because

of the prophecy that the king, his father, would be killed
by the hand of his son. Oedipus, however, was rescued and
brought up by foster parents, whom he believed to be his
own. As a young man he learns from an oracle that he
is destined to kill his father and marry his mother. Horrified,
he attempts to escape his fate by leaving what he believes
to be his home. On the journey he encounters a stranger,
an older man who provokes a fight and is killed by Oedipus.

When Oedipus arrives at the next city, he finds the citizens
in mourning for their king who, they believe, has been
killed by bandits. The man who can solve the riddle of the
Sphinx is to be their next king. Oedipus solves it, becomes
king, and marries the widowed queen. They have several
children during the years of his prosperous reign. Then a
plague descends upon the city, and the oracle says that it
will not be lifted until the slayer of the former king is
revealed. In his search for the truth, Oedipus discovers to
his horror that the stranger he killed was his own father,
the king, and that the mother of his children is also his
own mother. Oedipus puts out his eyes and staggers off
in self-banishment, and the queen kills herself.

The legend of Oedipus has lived on in history while other
dramas just as well written have been quickly forgotten,
for every man is subconsciously touched by the story.
Oedipus Rex is one of the first written dramas involved with
primordial sexual instincts and their subsequent repression
and expression in the evolving social order. Even today
primitive tribes have two basic taboos—against murder and
against incest.

The incest taboos in primitive tribes are so strong that
they extend to conduct with in-laws, and infractions are
punishable by death. A young husband, in some cases, is
forbidden to see or even walk in the footsteps of his mother-
in-law, and the same prohibition applies to a young wife
and her father-in-law. Rules regarding parents and children
of opposite sex, and brothers and sisters, are even more

strict. The validity of these taboos is evident in our modern society. In my own practice I have known cases in which a young wife divorced her young husband to marry her father-in-law (who subconsciously was a more satisfactory father substitute), and a young husband who was sexually attracted to his mother-in-law with whom he felt a more sincere love. Cases of incest within the immediate family still occur, especially between father and daughter, as will be discussed later in this chapter.

The instincts that form the basis of the Oedipus complex are older than the human race. They originated in man's primordial ancestors and still persist. The Oedipus phenomenon can be noted even in tribal animals such as seals, walrus, horses, deer. The universal appeal of Walt Disney's *Bambi*, for example, is no doubt due to the timelessness of its theme —the challenge of the young buck to the patriarch of the herd, his father, for possession of the does and their fawns. The effort of the females to gain the attention of the male leader can be noted, too.

As the human animal evolved he, too, lived in a tribal society dominated by an older and stronger male who had supreme authority over the females and their offspring. When the young females reached maturity, they mated with the patriarch, their father. When the young males matured, however, and desired to mate with the females, they were fought off by the father—who did not wish to lose his influence and harem—until finally one or more of the sons became strong enough to kill him or drive him off and take possession of the harem. All the females then belonged to the new young patriarch.

These primordial instinctual energies, stored in the subconscious, account for the infantile lust feelings toward the parent of the opposite sex and between brothers and sisters. It took millions of years for human society to evolve to its present status. The primary motivating force of evolution was the rebellion of the young males against the patriarch

in the attempt to create a social environment that more
readily satisfied their needs, sexual and otherwise.

When the sons deposed the patriarchal ruler, they began
to fight among themselves to determine who should take
the father's place. The discord and the feeling that each
was an unqualified usurper and less desirable than the original
father led to inherent feelings of hatred, guilt, and a longing
for the peacefulness of the life that existed under the father's
reign. Acts to appease the deposed father's spirit and seek his
return led to tribal rituals in primitive life.

Ultimately man turned to a single supreme being, the
father god, to whom he gave his loyal obedience. In man's
mind hate for authority exists side by side with love for it.
Resentment of environmental forces opposing his needs
intermingles with respect for these forces. Guilt for revolt
against established orders is fused with the need for punishment.

Because sexual adjustment is the key to subsequent life
adjustment, the way in which the Oedipus complex is
resolved determines the behavior patterns of adolescence
and maturity. Later influences may modify these, but the
basic patterns of childhood repeat themselves throughout
life. The instinct for repetition causes the individual to
relive his first unfulfilled and repressed Oedipus love life
over and over again. When the Oedipus complex is normally
resolved, the later adult love life will be rewarding.

Both parents should meet the child's affectionate need
directly and warmly, but not possessively. The loved parent
should respond to the sensual needs by helping him suppress
and redirect them in ways that enhance normal sexual
growth. Undue encouragement or discipline for activities
in one stage or another of sexual development may arrest
the child's sexuality.

The parent of the same sex as the child should be the one
administering the strongest discipline so that the child does

not come to regard punishment as a rejection by the loved parent because of the child's sensual desires.

The child should not sleep with the loved parent. When the opposing parent occupies this place, the child learns by example that his sensual feelings are not acceptable and also that he must learn to use them in an appropriate way. The parents should express their love for each other openly. A gift, some praise, a kiss, and a hug between the parents not only help the child to control his Oedipus feelings but also give a sense of warmth and security that will stay with the child into adult life and influence his own marital relations. When the parents share their love with their child in affectionate expression, after their own embrace, the moment will be long remembered and treasured.

In this kind of family atmosphere, the child's Oedipus complex resolves itself normally. It becomes obvious that the early Oedipus longings are not compatible with reality, and the conscious mind represses them in a natural, normal manner. These repressed desires are used to develop a mature sexuality. Then when the individual becomes an adult, he finds a mate who resembles the loved parent—often in appearance, usually in predominant character traits. Such marriages are usually happy ones. Not only does the spouse provide compassion, understanding, warmth, and material necessities, as the parent did, but added to this love is sexual gratification. The first love object evolves into the complete love object of maturity, fulfilling all the instinctual and conscious needs and wishes of human sexuality.

What mothers—and fathers, too—must guard against is "over-love," or "smother-love," as it is sometimes called. Parents who do everything for their children cripple them emotionally. In later life, children raised in this way are unable to separate themselves from parental affection and authority. Although they may later find individuals whom they love, impotence is often a problem because they subconsciously are oriented to nonsexual parent-child love. Individuals who are overly attached to parents usually make a better adjustment with older spouses to whom they can more easily transfer their love. These people have a tremendous need for affection and are highly dependent upon the presence of the loved one, developing feelings of insecurity and anxiety even during short separations.

Mary B is a case in which the child did not receive adequate affection from the parent and tries to attract by other means. Mary's father worked late hours. When he left early in the morning he was too rushed and when he came home at night too tired to pay much attention to her. When her parents retired to bed and sent Mary to her room, she subconsciously felt that she was being punished for her instinctual desires to give her father a baby. Her Electra frustrations expressed themselves in dreams of sleeping with, being caressed by, and having babies of men who symbolically represented her father. She frequently dressed up in her mother's clothes and played house with a neighbor's younger boy as the father, lying down beside him at "play bedtime."

These outlets, however, were not sufficient. To attract her father's personal attention, Mary began doing things to aggravate him. The more he corrected her for biting her nails, for example, or pulling at her hair, the more she repeated these and other actions that annoyed him. When he punished her, she only increased the "bad habits," which provoked much close personal contact with him. Disturbed by his daughter's apparent antagonism, Mary's father then made efforts to please and conciliate her. These affectionate gestures, of course, gave her the attention she needed.

Thus, early in childhood, Mary subconsciously learned an identity of opposites—that love can beget hate, and hate can beget love. This lesson and the resultant pattern that she established with her father stayed with her throughout life. As an adult she was always attracted to men who showed her little attention. She would seek out such men at parties and find ways of annoying them. Her usual method was to make such a public fuss over the man that out of embarrassment he was forced to give her attention. She never failed to give him her phone number and address. If he followed through, Mary told all her friends—and if the man was married, his wife—that he was trying to become intimate with her.

Even now, although she is married and the mother of three children, Mary continues this pattern of behavior. She is not being deliberately malicious in forcing her attentions on men and then gossiping about them when they make the obvious response. What she is doing is subconsciously re-enacting the childhood game with her father—but the men who try to "make" her are not playing the game correctly. Her father never followed up his kisses with anything more than a pat on the head. How dare these men do otherwise? Mary cannot understand how they get the impression that she is "that kind of woman."

Julia's case is in direct contrast. Now twenty-nine, she has been married and divorced three times, each marriage lasting only several months. Between marriages, she has consistently lived as a common-law wife and her present common-law husband is the man whom she last divorced. They have been very happy for several years and are now considering remarriage. Julia, however, fears to take this step. As she explains it, she does not feel "comfortable" and cannot enjoy sex relations with a man to whom she is legally wed. She loves her formerly legal, now common-law husband but becomes nervous and depressed at the thought of remarrying him—although she does not understand why.

Julia's Electra complex, only partially repressed in early childhood, was abnormally resolved at age ten, when her father seduced her. Her genital sexual relations with him have continued ever since, even during her marriages. Although her father is now elderly and a widower, Julia admits candidly that she continues to have intercourse with him at infrequent intervals.

This unnatural love experience with her father established the pattern that Julia continued to follow with lovers of her own age. Although she has never had any guilt feelings about having sex with her father, to marry him would be personally and socially devastating to her. She cannot marry the father substitutes, either, without becoming extremely upset emotionally. Julia's problem cannot be solved unless she can develop an understanding of it within herself. Explaining it to her may help to guide her, but it will not effect a cure—and it is questionable whether a cure can be affected after her early injury.

Boys are seldom seduced by their mothers, but their Oedipus feelings toward the mother are usually intense. A sense of rejection or betrayal by the mother can have a devastating effect. Neglect of the child can produce a sense of total rejection in the child. The instinctive reaction to real or fancied rejection is aggressive anger, as when the baby bites his mother's nipple when she has delayed his feeding time. In extreme cases, the subconscious resentment may build up an "identity of opposites." The initial love becomes aggressive hate, which can reach such overwhelming proportions that matricide (murder of the mother) results. Such repressed love converted into aggressiveness frequently masks itself behind extreme courtesy and obedience. News stories appear of the "nice quiet boy" who suddenly "went berserk" and "for no apparent reason" murdered one or both parents or raped an older woman.

With proper guidance, the Oedipal energies can be directed into constructive channels—such as achievements in business, politics, sports, or the creative arts. As noted earlier in this chapter, the father-son hostility component of the Oedipus complex has been the prime motivating force in the evolution of human civilization. It is responsible for mankind's progress from the small primordial tribe to the freely organized governmental systems of our Western democracies today; from the worship of a multiplicity of nature gods to the realization of a universal intelligence; from a strictly animal sexuality whose sole purpose was reproduction of the species to a specifically human sexuality in which the mental and emotional components are more significant than the physical. Today's alarming trend toward degrading this evolved sexuality and retrogressing to the primordial stage is, to a large extent, due to an unresolved Oedipus complex condition prevalent in the last two generations.

IX

~~~~~~

Generation Gap

As his qualifications for writing *Through Darkest Adolescence*, Richard Armour cited the fact that—although he hated to admit it—he had once been a teen-ager himself and was now the father of several. To these same basic requirements, let me add some twenty years of intense medical practice along with being the referral physician for the school district in a typical urban community. From this clinical experience, I believe—in spite of the volumes that have been written for and about teen-agers—the reasons for teenage behavior have been pitifully misinterpreted.

For youth, growing up means liberation from childhood dependencies. The process involves devaluating the family. Inwardly, however, the need for dependency remains, causing a fear of losing the parent. This fear turns into anger which is projected onto parents and adult authorities.

I have never been able to become blasé about the recurrent problems of adolescence, most of which center on the intense desire to become an independent adult.

The story of the preacher's daughter who was brought up with strict virtue but becomes a prostitute may be old hat, but in real life it keeps happening and is tragic for the girl and her parents. Sue Ann exemplifies such a case.

Sue Ann was a young lady of fourteen, whom I had

delivered at birth. During her childhood, I had treated her for childhood illnesses, taken out her tonsils, strapped the ankle she sprained roller skating—all the things that a family doctor does for a chid while she is growing up. Sue Ann was now in her second year junior high, plodding through her studies with low passing grades, as usual. Her dislike of school and studying was not caused by stupidity or the distraction of outside activities; it was actually a subconscious rebellion against overly strict parental authority.

Sue Ann's mother and father were "good, God-fearing people." They were staunch pillars of their church—a stern denomination that frowned upon dancing and other such frivolities of the flesh. Exacting as they were about their daughter's behavior, however, Sue Ann's parents felt a genuine affection for her. They provided her with a comfortable home, good clothes, wholesome food, and, they believed, healthy outlets for her emotions. Though her parents had married in their teens and did not go beyond high school, they planned a college education for Sue Ann.

They and her teachers constantly nagged her about poor grades. She, however, did not feel that better grades were important to her happiness. Instead, she saw that attaining them would be doing what they wanted, not what she wanted.

"Learning just comes hard for some children," Sue Ann's mother used to apologize. "But we can't complain. Sue Ann is a good, quiet girl. She minds us and never gives us any trouble."

But trouble was certainly in the air that afternoon when the three of them came into my office—the mother distressed, the father grim, Sue Ann defiant.

It was this smoldering defiance of parental restrictions that failed to take into account a child's needs that had finally demanded release and precipitated the present crisis. Sue Ann was pregnant. She had deliberately become so. Her parents —who had disapproved of her interest in boys and especially

of her boyfriend Willy—had finally forbidden her to see
him at all. This parental prohibition had made the young
people all the more determined to be together. Willy was
two years older than Sue Ann and as rebellious against school
as she was. He wanted to quit and get a job, but his parents
would not let him. Believing themselves to be very much
in love with each other, Willy and Sue Ann decided to
declare their independence and force parental consent to
their marriage by becoming parents themselves.

Looking at Sue Ann, who still seemed like a child to me,
it was difficult for me to think of her engaging in sexual
intercourse. Thinking of the sixteen-year-old Willy, it
seemed more natural. Their situation was unusual, because
as a rule in teen-age pregnancies the last thing the boy wants
to do is to marry the girl. In this case, however, it was Sue
Ann's parents who were adamantly opposed to it. They
considered Willy "shiftless and immoral."

"Marriage is out of the question," declared Sue Ann's
mother. "The situation is disgraceful enough as it is, but it
can be handled. Sue Ann, of course, cannot have her baby
in this city. Before her condition becomes apparent, she and
I will take a trip. We have come to you, Dr. Anchell, to
ask you to recommend a place for us to go to, where everything can be taken care of quietly, and the baby put up
for adoption."

Sue Ann was in tears. She thought she was weeping because a cruel fate was separating her from her "true love."
Actually, however, her almost hysterical sobs sprang from
the frustration of her instincts of mastery and self-determination—once again thwarted and trapped by what she felt was
a rigid authority contemptuously disregarding her needs.
Like every child, Sue Ann wanted the affection and approval of her elders, but their demands seemed to serve
only themselves, not her. The parental and religious code
required dutiful devotion, to the exclusion of activities

enjoyed by her schoolmates such as dances and dates. At school her teachers were always pressing her to improve her grades, and their wishes were more than she was capable of meeting. As a result, her resentment turned against all of them, and she subconsciously seized upon Willy—the victim of similar repressions—as her means of escape.

Sue Ann had been taught that "nice girls" did not have babies out of wedlock. Therefore, if she became pregnant, her parents would let her marry Willy, and she would be free from their domination, free from the dictates of school, and free from criticism by the church. Her conscious mind —indoctrinated as it was—did not accept these wishes directly, but in the disguised form of "being in love." In reality, Sue Ann did not love Willy, and in all probability their marriage would have disintegrated once its true purpose was served.

Because of the subconscious motives behind the pregnancy, as well as the emotional problems related to the pregnancy itself, I advised Sue Ann's parents to approve the marriage. Even a short-lived marriage, I felt, would be less traumatic than the parents' course of action.

My advice, however, was not heeded. Sue Ann's parents felt sincere in doing what they thought best for their daughter, but actually their motivations and authority were in accord wih their interests, not hers. Through their mishandling of the situation, they increased Sue Ann's resentment and lost her respect. She discovered that "nice girls" could have babies out of wedlock without disgrace—as long as no one outside the family knew about it. Marriage was not the sacrosanct institution her parents and the church had said it was. Sue Ann had her first lesson—always a shock to the young—in the hypocrisy of an adult moral code which is far more concerned about avoiding the appearance of evil than the evil itself. In the candid appraisal of youth, it is not adult words but actions which count—not "do as

I say," but "do as I do." Children raised by improper authorities are taught idealism but observe hypocrisy. They find it impossible to adjust to both.

Carmela's background, for instance, was in direct contrast to Sue Ann's, but the results were very similar. Carmela's mother was a gay divorcée, who warned her teen-age daughter about the dangers of necking and gave other advice about behavior with boys. But the mother herself neglected to be circumspect in relations with her men friends. Pleased that her daughter was popular and duly advised, she let Carmela use her own judgment about dating.

Early one morning when I arrived at my office, I found a frightened Carmela awaiting me.

"Dr. Anchell, please help me!" she cried. "I can't tell my mother—and I'm bleeding."

The night before, after some heavy necking in a parked car, her date had given the ultimatum, "Go down—or out!"

Carmela went down. And when she got up from her first experience at mating, she started bleeding. This occasionally happens when the hymen, the membrane which partially closes the vaginal opening, is intemperately stretched in virginal girls. It was something, however, which Carmela did not know about. The girl was in panic, and the boy was angry. He drove Carmela home as fast as he could and dropped her unceremoniously on her doorstep. Although it was late, Carmela's mother had not yet returned from her own date. Equipped with a sanitary napkin, the trembling Carmela got into bed and pretended to be asleep when her mother came home. Early in the morning she slipped out quietly and hurried to my office.

"You aren't popular if you don't neck," Carmela sobbed. "My mother tells me not to—but I've seen her do it."

Professional ethics, of course, required that I notify Carmela's mother. She acted suprised and at a loss to understand the reason for her daughter's conduct.

Carmela and Sue Ann are only two of the many thousands

of teen-age girls who engage in premature genital sex experiences. Some get pregnant, some don't. Some who get pregnant have babies, others have abortions that may maim them for life. With all, the mental and emotional scars are permanent.

My clinical experience confirms Dr. Albert Kinsey's findings and show that teen-age girls actually have an aversion to sexual intercourse. Then why do so many of them do it?

In the challenge to adult authority, the adolescent identifies with the adults about him and attempts to outdo them at their own games.

The game that adults play that is consistently forbidden to children is sexual intercourse. Therefore, overthrowing this taboo becomes the greatest immediate fulfillment of youthful instincts for mastery and self-determination, particularly in the male.

Though the boy's sexual activity is extroverted, no such urgency exists in the average female adolescent. Virginal girls, however, are curious as to what they are missing. Their normal sexual curiosity finds imaginative answers in sex fantasies and dreams, although these seldom involve the actual sex act. The superstition that thoughts and actions are the same—although in reality they are not—causes some girls to develop feelings that they have actually enjoyed in their lust fantasies. The desire to experience the imaginary passions gives them the false impression that the reality will be just like the dreams. As in the song "How Does the Wine Taste?" they conclude that it "tastes good," even though they have never tried it. Actually, wine doesn't taste good until the desire and taste for it have been cultivated. Even then it must be served properly or else one drinks without pleasure and like an alcoholic destroys himself. The analogy may be applied to the sex act and women.

As noted, the male has a natural taste for the wine of sex. His task is to persuade the female to enjoy it with him —to convince her that by abstaining she is depriving herself of an ecstatic thrill that is far more important than morality.

Beginning with the sexual emancipation of the 1920s, this task of persuasion has become easier and easier. Teen-age boys have "never had it so good" as they do today. Their arguments find support throughout our culture and customs —and most conveniently in the entertainment media. Before making their pitch, the boys can soften up the girls with a "good," contemporary movie or play or with radio music or stereo so suggestive that it would make a harem dancer blush.

Everything seems to conspire on behalf of the male to break down the female's instinctive resistance and cause her to lead a sex life satisfying the boy's lust. The girls are brain-washed by misinformation and disoriented sexual advice into believing that they should feel the same sexual compulsions as boys and that their own natural inhibitions are erroneous. In the general attitude of society, free indulgence in sexual rela-tions is in, chastity is out. Virginal girls are made to feel chastity is due to prudishness or immaturity.

The old story of the schoolboy's essay on "The Pleasures of Childhood" is especially apt today. After enumerating various innocent boyhood joys, the young author concluded with the classic statement: "But great as are the pleasures of childhood, they are nothing compared to the pleasures of adultery."

To modern youth, the words *adult* and *adulterer* are practically synonymous. Following the example of many parents, as well as emulating the popular heroes and heroines of current fiction, motion pictures, and television, the young are striving to "out-adulterate" the adults.

The result of unnatural sexual relationship is the increas-ing dissatisfaction of both sexes. As we have discussed, over the millions of years of human evolution the human being has acquired an instinctive mental component of sexuality. Although modern males are enjoying a heyday of physical sex, they remain unsatisfied when the mental ingredient is not present.

The girl needs to be psychologically ready for intercourse. She cannot skip the stages necessary for this psychological sexual preparation without blighting her emotional life. She remains entangled in infantile feelings. Prematurely indulging in intercourse interferes with achieving complete normal femininity and later motherhood. These conditions are becoming devastatingly prevalent.

Sexual relations may allow a girl to consider herself emancipated; but instead of becoming a free human being, she becomes enslaved to unresolved unconscious urges and fantasies.

You cannot prevent your child from going through adolescence or from identifying with contemporaries. You can, however, prepare him for weathering these storms by helping him from infancy onward to develop his survival instincts in a healthy, natural manner. Beneficent authority, which teaches by its own example rather than by dictum, inspires the children's confidence and respect. Affectionate understanding strengthens the bonds of family love and loyalty. Under such influences, the child's conscious mind reaches its highest development in conscientiousness. This conscience is a form of moral reality that establishes guidelines for the individual's conduct and his relations with others. Although the adolescent may temporarily stray from these guidelines in his overzealous efforts to prove his capacity for independence, his conscience will inevitably bring him back and set him on a well-adjusted path to maturity.

As with everything, it is possible to overdo even good things. If the conscience becomes overly developed, it inhibits the normal progress of the individual in his adjustment to social changes. He becomes static, rooted in the social morality of his earlier life. Instead of adjustable guidelines based on reality, his conscience has forged chains that bind him to outmoded customs. When such an individual becomes a parent, he imposes unrealistic regulations on his children, as in the case of Sue Ann.

Adolescents who have been dominated by cruel authority during their formative years break away with the most explosive force. A similar reaction occurs in children having overly permissive parents. Higher education does not modulate their behavior. College students of this type create just as many problems as do high school dropouts. They have little or no affectionate allegiance to the authoritative forces of their childhood. Their antisocial behavior represents a constant revenge upon these authorities, expressed in attacks on society in general.

The overall attitude of society toward the "anything goes" revolt, however, is the result of the overswing of progressivism toward a complete lack of authority. In permissive environments teen-age extremists find little resistance. Their abreaction becomes excessive. Their sex life becomes more profuse, varied, and perverted than that of the general adult population. They attack adult authority where it is most vulnerable, throwing back the teachings and influences of their elders.

The teen-ager, trying to determine who he is, searches for new relationships, that is, new objects to love, hate, and identify with outside the family. The identifications provide ego ideals who are admired and emulated.

In a normal environment, the family and community have similar moral standards and it is not difficult for the adolescent to make satisfactory identifications.

By the age of twenty or twenty-one, the average individual reestablishes his family background and incorporates it with the identifications made during adolescence. This fusion is responsible for creating the adult's personality. Ideally, it reflects the best of childhood and adolescent influences. Unfortunately, trying to fuse family values with today's standards is similar to mixing water with oil. Bachelor mothers, communal families, perverts, and drug users reflect the compromises of many youths.

Actually, history is repeating itself, although at a faster pace and on a larger world stage. The antiauthority revolt of a postwar generation is always excessive. Although the rigid restrictions of wartime are tolerated during the emergency, a subconscious and often conscious resentment builds up throughout the population against the absolutism of wartime military and government authority. As soon as the war ends and these restraints are lifted, pent-up instinctual energies gush forth in a flood that tears away much of the existing social structure.

The explosion of the 1960s in the aftermath of World War II was not unlike the upheaval of the 1920s in the aftermath of World War I. The reaction, however, was much greater in degree—a difference that might be symbolically measured by the differences between the flapper's knee-high skirt and her granddaughter's miniskirt.

The postwar collapse of moral standards is accompanied by an indignant rebellion of youth against adult hypocrisy under the moral code. Today's adolescent, for example, has been taught by adults that excessive drinking is harmful and morally wrong—yet he sees teachers, parents, or other adults in his immediate sphere, increasing their intake of alcohol year by year. Movies, books, and plays produced by adults glorify debased living. Youth listen to the adult appeal for courtesy, brotherly love, and understanding in human relations, but see their elders fighting verbally and physically among themselves, and learn from adult-produced TV programs and other media that to be a man you have to have the fastest gun or the hardest fists. They are told that "might does not make right," but find out that dictatorial power controls the destinies of men and nations. They are brought up to believe in the virtues of matrimony, but discover that adultery and divorce are the order of things in adult life

The adolescent has been encouraged to redirect his own instincts by adult authority. Now he becomes aware that
the adult world has been using that authority as a screen
behind which it vents its repressions. In revulsion against
this hypocrisy, he vehemently swings the pendulum of behavior in the opposite direction. He makes no bones about
being out for himself—and watch out if you get in the
way! In outdoing the adult he has established no boundaries.
Not for him the marriage farce—shack up with anybody,
anytime, anywhere! If you need money, rob a bank. If you
need material things, sack the local stores the next time there
is a race riot. No wonder the crime rate has increased in all
countries to an all-time high! In the United States alone,
statistics show that each year 2,500,000 youngsters between
the ages of eleven and nineteen appear before the juvenile
courts for delinquency. There are, of course, many more who
are not brought before the courts.

Undoubtedly, as in the 1930s, inertia will cause the pendulum to swing back to a more natural and healthy way of
life. As in the 1920s, the 1970s are forcing man to re-
examine himself and his relations with his fellow humans.
What is needed is not a return to dictatorial authority nor
a complete relaxation or absence of authority, but the balance
of a firm authority whose primary concern is to guide and
help those under its jurisdiction to make a correct, natural
adjustment within themselves and within the community
of man. This is the ideal type of authority on every level,
from parent to government. Our country continues to flour-
ish, in spite of its imperfections and mistakes, because the
American system is basically oriented toward this ideal. This
goal cannot be achieved on a national basis, however, until
it is first achieved within the family unit.

X

~~~~~~

The Psychedelic Revolution

Beatniks, hippies, yippies, and other such breeds have the same psychological characteristics. Anxious to prove themselves unique, each group displays its own particular peculiarities in dress and mannerisms. Like branches on a tree, however, they all arise from the same roots. The basis for their personalities stems from an inability to adjust to the needs for independence and sex.

Hippie Independency

The desire to be independent begins at birth and continues throughout life. It can be observed in infancy when the infant resists the mother feeding him. He cries, holds his breath, and refuses food until he is allowed to use the spoon and feed himself. When ineptness at self-feeding finally causes hunger to overcome self-determination, he again turns to his parent for help. Even then, he is not happy with dependency, and poor eating habits may result.

Like an impending revolution, the independence urge builds up throughout childhood until in adolescence it explodes with volcanic force. The intensity of the dependency rebellion varies from a normal testing-out of self mastery within the framework of the family background to a total destruction of all previous standards.

Much of the startling behavior of some present-day young adults is a result of this inborn need to stand on one's own two feet. Though the wish is normal, the resultant uncontrolled behavior in some cases is not.

Paradoxically, the more violently the individual overthrows established systems, the more he subconsciously fears relying on himself and losing the parent's help.

Just as the gorilla ferociously beats his chest to bluff those who frighten him, the pseudo independent hippie tries to hide his fear of taking his place in society by flaunting his disdain for conventionalities. In reality the hippie is scared to death and if his bluff is called he falls apart.

Hippie Sex

During adolescence there is a resurgence of affectionate and physical love interest. Memories of the first love experience—the infantile Oedipal love for the parent—arise from the subconscious mind. Youth progressing normally through childhood stages of sexual growth find little difficulty in repressing these incestual memories.

The normal adolescent reinvests earlier affectionate and sensual love for the parent in individuals outside the family. The new love frequently resembles the parent in many ways. With the Oedipus feeling resolved, the ego and conscience are not in conflict with subconscious sex desires.

Hippie youths are the ones whose sexual growth is usually stunted. It can be reasonably assumed that hippies suffer from unresolved Oedipal complexes. During adolescence, when these feelings come up into the conscious mind, intense anxiety develops. The hippie's sexual behavior reflects his efforts to repress incestual urges.

His devaluation of parents and parent types is more complete than is normally the case. Love for parents may be converted into hate. He finds it difficult to become sensually involved with members of the opposite sex who resemble the parent ideal. Though he may involve himself in affectionate relationships with these idealized types, the incest barrier in the mind incapacitates him for physical relationships with them. To help push back the Oedipus into the subconscious, he may develop resistance to all potential love objects or authorities that are identified with the parents. His capacity for love becomes limited to engaging in affectionless physical relationships with "love objects" who are most unlike the parents in all ways.

This "identity of opposites reaction" was responsible for the older beatnik generation's choosing as parental substitutes dirty, unkempt, and promiscuous members of the opposite sex. These love mates were most unlike the meticulous, chaste parents of the 1930s. The males with tangled beards, the females with long uncombed hair lived together in pads. Their squalor was a dreamlike disguise of their previous family life.

For the beatnik-hippie's children—now adolescents—to debase their parental ideal still further would seem to be something even an unresolved Oedipus complex could not accomplish. Hippie offspring, whose sexual development is even more completely arrested, have produced parental substitutes whose very sex is disguised. We now have girl-boys and boy-girls. They are clean—the opposite of the parents—and about as far removed from motherly and fatherly types as the "identity of opposites reaction" can allow.

It is difficult to tell which sex is which from their external appearance. The girl-boys dress like boys, act like boys, and even use perfume that smells like aftershave lotion. They affect a so-called "natural" makeup that further deemphasizes their feminity in its resemblance to a death mask. Some of the boy-girls are considerate enough to wear beards so it is possible to distinguish their real sex without examining their genitals. They use cologne and wear long hair, which is often coiffed at the same beauty salon as their sex partners'. They have not yet relinquished the wearing of pants.

When individuals engage in sex relations with partners totally unlike the ideal first love object, the sex act is purely physical. Affection is not expressed. In hippie language *love* is synonymous with *carnality*. Because of the unrequited affectionate component of sexuality, the hippies' physical sex relations build up a series of frustrations which may cause an impotence for genital intercourse. To escape from these frustrations and fear of impotence, they may indulge in promiscuities such as continually changing partners. Sexual frustration may reach such a point of disgust that these youths turn to direct perversions of homosexuality or other perverted acts. Why pretend to have natural relationships with the opposite sex when in reality these relations are unnaturally incomplete? Since perversities are recognized as unnatural to begin with, it seems to the hippie more justifiable—an "honest" perversion, not a hypocritical one.

The sexual life of the hippie is replete with perversities. Filthy expressions and indecent four-letter words are used to promote infantile oral-anal sex pleasures. Their literature and conversation are largely involved with themes related to genital anatomy, sexual intercourse, and reproduction. These subjects stimulate them in the same way young children are excited by this type of information. The hippie is usually shoeless; he openly admires his dirty feet. Many perverts subconsciously regard the feet in a phallic way, just as animals use the sense of smell as stimulus for sex. The hippie is greatly aroused by nudity. Sensual pleasure from exhibitionism and voyeurism is a chief source of his sexual satisfaction. (Normally, the female is more inclined to exhibitionism and the male to voyeurism. This fact accounts for the go-go, topless, and burlesque establishments having female performers and male audiences.)

The micro-mini-skirted hippie does not dress for fashion, but for the sensual excitement she feels from exhibiting the intimate parts of her body. She may engage in sex acts for material gain, to conceal frigidity, or because of obligations.

During intercourse she may learn to make sensual noises and to use her vaginal muscles for a simulated climax to please the male's ego. Her orgasm, however, is usually feigned since her primary sex interest is not genital.

Rehabilitation of the hippie is difficult. To give up his means of gratifying sexual needs and attempt to make a normal adjustment is a terrifying task. Since there is no guarantee that his psychosexuality can be resolved and mature sexuality attained, "Why give up a bird in the hand?" Compounding this resistance is the subconscious fear that the sensual pleasure from normal relationships may fail to be as satisfying as perversions.

Hippies have had the unfortunate experience of having parents, society, or both fail in helping them to grow up. This failure may result from lack of parental affection or parental overpossessiveness, an under- or overdeveloped conscience, too little or too many material advantages, over-permissiveness for sex activities or unrealistic punishment for childhood sensual indulgences, promiscuious contemporaries, drug-using friends, and, especially, premature seductions by actual attacks or by pornography.

Hippies and Drugs

Preteen children expend sensual pleasure in Oedipal fantasies. The 6-12-year-old knows that sexual relations with parents are forbidden and the real identities of the parent and child are disguised—at first as the prince and princess of fairy tales, or as the hero or heroine who rescues the beloved and performs noble acts of sacrifice. As the child reaches pre-puberty and learns more about the realities of sex, the disguises change. The boy learns about the existence of "loose women" who mate promiscuously. In his fantasies of this period, his parental love object and he himself take the forms of a prostitute and her paramour. In the girl's fantasies at this stage the roles are reversed. To disguise her incestuous feelings toward her father, she becomes the "loose woman" and he a degraded man. All young people normally go through this phase of feeling lust for lewd women or gigolos. Under normal conditions it quickly passes into a natural resolution of the Oedipus complex and, as previously explained, sensual desires are redirected toward fulfillment with a second love object who resembles the loved parent in real life, personifying the ideal woman or man.

The sexually active but frustrated hippie is prone to return to childhood sexual pleasures. However, the imaginations of adolescents and adults are not capable of conjuring up fantasies as easily as those of children. To recreate erotic fantasies, hippies use hallucinatory agents. Love children, "turned on" by the effects of banana peels, glue, marijuana, LSD, tranquilizers, uppers, or downers, become "high." Their chemically conditioned brains are now capable of developing vivid fantasies and dreams. During his psychedelic sex trips, the drugged hippie may have an orgasm by means of masturbating himself or through mutual masturbation with companions.

Hippie Contagion

The depressing situation of these unhappy hippie adolescents does not mean that all teen-agers who follow the prevalent hippie fads in dress, dance, and music are in the same predicament. However, even the mentally healthy adolescent, who maintains the guidance he receives from normal parents and who has developed a natural sexual maturation, will be harmed to a certain extent by subsequent exposure and association.

The herd instinct is especially strong during the teens. It is impossible to keep a youngster from participating in the activities of his own age group. In his compulsion to become an adult—to act independently—the average teen-ager overdoes it at first. If home influences are wholesome, he normally recovers from this abreaction and becomes a well-adjusted adult. He will not be quite the same, of course. It is like recovering from an illness such as pneumonia. Under proper treatment the healthy patient gets well. He acquires scars, but he also develops an immunity to reinfection.

The social instinct in adolescents is one of the strongest and can cause antisocial behavior, irrespective of a youth's having been raised with proper values from parents. The following letter points up this fact. The letter was written on behalf of a young man arrested for selling drugs. Names and places have been changed for obvious reasons.

MELVIN ANCHELL, M.D., ABFP
11633 San Vicente Boulevard, Suite 320
Los Angeles, California 90049

Robert Miller, Attorney
456 Callo Street
Nestle,
California 90025

Dear Mr. Miller:

Mrs. Charles Smith has asked that I send you my findings regarding her son, John. Mrs. Smith brought John to see me for an interview October 23, 1970. Though I had only one session with him, I feel the following evaluation is substantially correct.

John reveals a strong love attachment for the mother. His respect for the father is affected by intense antagonism due to his parent's stalwart authoritativeness.

The preadolescent family environment provided moral and religious standards creating a well-developed conscience in the patient.

Adolescent identifications with contemporaries, permissiveness in his community, and military experiences have made a realistic adjustment in accord with family values difficult for him. John's conscience is oriented toward "right and wrong," but his conscious mind is greatly influenced by the current social practices of directly expressing inner desires without regard to conscience. However, in "doing his own thing," he develops anxieties which keep him from disregarding the effect of his behavior on others. The recent episode, involving his selling narcotics, is, in my opinion, contrary to John's usual character. The direct cause for this incident was his enthrallment with the movie, *Easy Rider*.

The patient saw this picture three times. He developed an idealization of the hero and identified with him. He felt compelled to follow in the hero's footsteps. In the movie, the hero sells drugs to obtain money for a vagabond trip from California to New Orleans. John planned to make the identical trip in the same way.

I feel it is unlikely that John would again sell drugs or involve himself in unlawfulness. I believe, he will make a satisfactory personal adjustment that will enable him to live a useful and proper life.

Sincerely,

Melvin Anchell, M.D., ABFP

Hippie Love Sadists

"Make love, not war"—Charles Manson.

Roman Polanski, a prosperous motion picture director, owes much of his success to such forebodingly macabre movies as *Knife in the Water*, *Repulsion*, and *Rosemary's Baby*.

In *Rosemary's Baby*, Satan, wishing an heir incarnate to rival Jesus, rapes the heroine. An indelibly vivid scene shows the Devil engaged in sexual intercourse with Rosemary, impregnating her with his son.

In 1969 the actress wife of Polanski, Sharon Tate, was diabolically murdered in her Bel Air, California, home. Following her death, *Newsweek* quoted producer Polanski critically denouncing this nation, saying, "What kind of country! What kind of people!"

Certain psychological facts and circumstances involving

the Tate murders lead me to believe that the ghoulish killers took their cue from Polanski's films, especially *Rosemary's Baby*. The statement of Dr. Alberta E. Seigel made at a symposium on violence at the Stanford School of Medicine shows how it could happen.

. . . people watch not only the social behavior of other people around them, but also the behavior of individuals portrayed in the mass media—especially movies and TV.

Susan Atkins, a member of the hippie clan brought to justice for the murders, described her knowledge of the case in a December 14, 1969, *Los Angeles Times* copyrighted article:

Prior to the murders she and her drug-using cohorts, wearing black clothes called "creepy crawlies," entered strangers' houses and crawled around for experience. They wore these shrouds on the night of the Tate killings, which were motivated, Atkins said, to instill fear in a young man who had crossed her leader, Charles Manson.

The killers showed no mercy for their victims. Young Steven Parent, pleading "Please don't hurt me, I won't say anything," was shot four times and killed. When Voyteck Frykowski asked, "Who are you? What do you want?" Tex Watson, one of the hippies involved, answered "I'm the devil. I am here to do the devil's business." When Frykowski ran from the house, screaming for his life, he was stabbed incessantly, shot in the back and hit over the head, breaking the gun.

Abigail Folger, who readily surrendered to the killers, was stabbed repeatedly before dying. Sharon Tate, begging that her baby's life be spared, was held by the head and stabbed in the heart—again and again.

After the killings, Susan Atkins returned to her communal hippie quarters, had intercourse with someone whom she does not remember and went to sleep.

The following night, she and her group again killed. After taking an LSD trip, they entered the home of *Rosemary* LaBianca. [Italics mine.] Calling themselves devils, they unsparingly killed Mr. and Mrs. LaBianca. Until Rosemary LaBianca died, her main concern was for her husband. She pleaded over and over, "What are you doing to my husband?"

After these murders, the hippies used the LaBianca's bathroom. They then ate the food in the refrigerator. Using a large fork to pierce Mr. LaBianca's stomach and carving the word "War" on his chest, they patted his dog and left.

Susan Atkins said that during her participations in the killings she had been mesmerized by Manson. Psychological facts would indicate, however, that she had regressed to a primitive mental state typical of horde groups. Such cultures cause a diminishing of the individual personality and a compulsion to carry out the thoughts and feelings of the group leader.

Horde members give their confidence and love to their idealized leader. To members of the Manson "family," Charles Manson had become a deified father to be feared and loved by all. Susan Atkins and the others eroticized this deification with childlike Oedipal love. This is why they were swayed by a narcissistic, sadistic leader to carry out his wishes. Their sensually strengthened allegiances caused them to follow Manson's commands as though in a hypnotic trance. Manson had developed the animal magnestism of a primitive tribal chieftain.

It is conceivable that the devil-worshipping killers identified Sharon Tate's unborn child with Polanski's baby created in *Rosemary's Baby*. In primitive tribes, when the tribal chief dies, the heir is his youngest son. Perhaps these combined circumstances had psychological meanings to Manson and his family.

After the Fall

The youth of today, as well as the now confused adults, are finally becoming sickened by antisocial behavior. They hunger for values that will fulfill the needs not only of the individual but also of his society. Just as in the 1930s there was a swing back to a healthy normalcy after the excesses of the 1920s, so the 1970s are likely to bring a return to reality after the even greater overswing of the 1960s.

As in the past, the explosive, regressive revolt that has shaken our society for almost two decades will have served a useful purpose. It has opened the eyes and minds of our society and forced a reevaluation of human needs and standards.

Already the return to reality has been begun by youth itself. Many young people are making a definite leadership effort to rechannel aggressive energies from destructive to constructive behavior. The "Sons of Watts," for example, formerly a gang known as the "Sons of the Stronghold" who actively participated in the "Burn, baby, burn!" riots of 1965, are now even more actively working to bring order, cleanliness, economic progress—and hope—to their community. From various parts of the country, news items are appearing about students who have spontaneously formed groups to raise funds for the medical expenses of police officers, custodians, and others who have been attacked and injured by teen-age gang. In Los Angeles County—which has received world-wide notoriety about its "Sunset Strip"—three teen-age boys were recently awarded Carnegie Hero medals for risking their lives to save others.

At the University of California, on whose Berkeley campus a noisy student minority under a perverted leadership has made headlines, they are some eight thousand other students whose aggressive energies are channelled in the opposite direction. These young men and women are devoting afternoons, weekends, and vacations working to help others in disadvantaged areas not only in their own state but in many parts of the world. As the *Los Angeles Times* has noted:

"The revolutionary and beatnik groups are minuscule—but the

public hears about them," said the University's president. "None of the future, however, belongs to them. The future belongs to the many other young people—whom I call the Peace Corps type —who are working in places like Watts, in prisons and other social agencies trying to improve the society in which they live."

XI

~~~~~~

What Is Pleasure?

I wish I was a little rock, a-sittin' on a hill,
A-doin' nothin' all day long but jest a-sittin' still.
I wouldn't eat, I wouldn't sleep, I wouldn't even wash.
I'd sit all day and sit all night—and think of you, by gosh!

In the simplest terms, this little folk verse sums up the
two basic motivations of human nature—the desire to do
nothing and the desire to share this state of bliss with another.

According to Sigmund Freud, complete pleasure is the
absence of all excitation. It is an effortless existence—the
fulfillment of the instinctive desire of all life to return to
its original state of inactivity.

For thousands of years mankind has expressed its intuitive
knowledge of this pleasure principle in religious terms. The
highest human attainment is considered to be the cessation
of conflict, not only among human beings but within oneself. It is the complete release from care and want, from
stress or strain of any kind—the "peace that passeth understanding" of the Judeo-Christian Heaven, the Nirvana of
Buddhism. In his search for this infinite peace, man instinctively seeks the perfect equilibrium of death—the return to
the inorganic state—"dust unto dust."

Countering this death wish is the equally strong desire for immortality, eternal life. This identity of opposites—death and life—is reconciled in religion by the death of the body and the immortality of the soul or spirit in its highest or most metaphysical conception. This belief seems to be timeless and universal with mankind. In earlier civilizations, such as those of the Egyptians and the American Indians, food and weapons and other serviceable objects were buried with the dead to help them on their journey to the land of the spirit. Among primitive peoples the belief is more earthbound. Some tribes, for example, believe that the spirit of the departed continues its life by entering into an animal, a tree, a waterfall, even a rock, and this symbolic object then becomes sacred.

However it may be expressed, this inherent belief in a life after death evidences intuitive human knowledge of the natural physical laws of the universe and man's instinctive obedience to those laws. The first law of physics is that energy can neither be created nor destroyed. The sum total of all the energy of the universe remains eternally the same. Although this energy is borrowed and utilized by living matter, it eventually returns to its original source, and the cycle begins again.

Thus, physically as well as metaphysically, although the living organism dies, it is immortal. Its essence is indestructible. It lives from the beginning to the end of time.

In today's nuclear age, when the energy of one atom has been fearsomely demonstrated, it is not difficult to understand how living matter evolved. Infinitely more slowly and gently than a nuclear explosion, the energy of inorganic matter was activated by the sun into simple chemical combinations which, under favorable environmental conditions, produced organic or living matter.

These first one-celled forms of life—similar to bacteria and microscopic animalcules that exist today—reproduced themselves by simple fission, dividing into two parts, each identical with the original. In order to perpetuate themselves indefinitely, however, it became necessary for two cells of the same type to merge, to renew their chemical substances by fusing into one. This rejuvenated organism then divided into two cells, both identical, and the continuous process of fusion and fission was set in motion.

As changes in the environment occurred, these unicellular organisms had to make adaptations in order to survive. A membrane was formed as protection against extremes of cold and heat. It also transmitted stimuli to the organism, informing it of changes in temperature, the presence of food, or of a hostile organism that would consume it—the first reflex knowledge. As life and the environment became more complicated, more changes occurred. Cells came together in group formations, such as molds or lichens, the multicellular unit enhancing the life potential of all the cells within it.

From these cell groups evolved plants and the early forms of animal life. Gradually, through an infinite series of adaptations, more complicated forms of life developed—fish, amphibians, reptiles, birds, mammals, and, finally, that most complex of all creatures, man.

It was not only physical evolution that took place over these billions of years, but the more significant evolution of the mental apparatus. This does not refer to the brain. It refers to the mental energies of which the brain is merely the physical instrument.

Stored in the subconscious part of the human mental apparatus are all the instinctual energies acquired through evolution since life began on the planet Earth. As each new form made its adaptation for survival, it acquired a pattern of reaction that enabled it to counteract the hostile elements or forces in its environment. Through repetition, this survival pattern became an instinct—a part of the primitive mental apparatus transmitted not only from generation to generation, but also to subsequent evolutionary forms of life.

For example, the first human sensory perception is touch, which harks back to that first protective membrane of the earliest unicellular organisms.

With every change of environment and every development of a new life form or species, new survival instincts have been added. The accumulation of these instinctual energies has become the eternal heritage of each species and of the succeeding higher forms of life. This process has continued from the beginning of life up to this very day and minute. As noted, for example, the first reaction of one-celled life was and is a response to changes in temperature. Billions of years up the scale of evolution are the wild geese, who fly south in the winter and north in the summer, assuring themselves of the most favorable climate for survival. No one tells the geese to do this, and they did not go to school to learn it. It is an instinct as valid for geese today as it was for their remote ancestors who averted extinction by fleeing the hostile winter of the northern nesting grounds. Early man made similar migrations, until the discovery of fire made possible a different adaptation and the acquisition of a new instinct, that of hearth and home. But the ancient instinct still persists—as attested to by flourishing winter resorts such as those in Florida and southern California.

Why do mature salmon swim thousands of miles through the ocean, up rivers and waterfalls, over dams, to the very streamlet of their origin, there to spawn and die? Instinctual energy drives them. The compulsion comes from some ancient time when such a trek meant survival of the species. This instinct, too, finds its echo in man, in the prevalent human wish to be buried in the land, and even the town, where one was born.

Such instincts are governed by two fundamental laws of nature known in physics as the law of inertia and the law of repetition.

The law of inertia concerns the basic characteristics of all matter, inorganic as well as organic, first to resist change and—when change does occur—to return to the original state. A chemical solution, for example, if left standing long enough, will separate into its basic components. This is the reason for the common direction, "Shake well before using." You can demonstrate it yourself with a simple solution of salt and water. As we have discussed, this law of inertia applies all the way up the scale of evolution from inorganic matter to man himself. In living organisms it is called the death instinct.

The law of repetition is fundamental in the continuous cycle of life and death. It governs the behavior of all living organisms. By repetition of inherited instincts, the indivdual organism seeks to master its environment and to determine its own course of life until it arrives at death in the manner characteristic of its species. In this compulsive effort to complete its natural life cycle, it will attempt to overcome every obstacle and hazard (as in the case of the salmon), it will flee from danger (rabbits, for example), it will fight for its food and for its life (predatory creatures, including man). All this accumulated experience is passed along in the form of instinctual energies and perpetuated indefinitely through the mental apparatus—from generation to generation within the same species, and from a lower to a higher form of life in the ascending scale of evolution. These subconscious instincts are the determining factors in behavior.

To realize how compelling these instincts are, consider how difficult it is to change even a habit—such as smoking —that has been acquired over a period of comparatively few years. An instinct is a habit that has become ingrained in living organisms over a period of many thousands to billions of years.

All life repeats itself. Nowhere is this more dramatically demonstrated than in the human embryo. Each human life begins as life began, with the fusion of two separate cells. The female ovum and the male sperm, each containing half the necessary chemicals and chromosomes (which carry the "blueprint" of the human being), unite to form a new and complete "seed" cell. This cell divides, and, by the continuing process of fission, groups of cells are formed, which resemble primitive multicellular organisms. As these cell groups organize and develop into the complex structure of the human body, the growing embryo passes through all the successive stages of evolution. Embryos developing through the fish stage, for example, possess fishlike gills. Normally these gills disappear before birth, but in some cases they remain as branchial clefts that must be corrected by surgery. At another stage the hands appear as birdlike wings, which develop into human hands and fingers as the arms elongate. If there is incomplete development of any specialized group or groups of cells, deformities result. Normally at the end of nine months, a completely formed human emerges from the womb.

This newborn infant is as old as the first man—in fact, as old as life itself. He has already relived billions of years of evolution. More than that, he brings with him—in the subconscious storehouse of his mental apparatus—all the instinctual energies that have accumulated since life began.

Some of these instincts will serve him well in meeting the problems he begins to encounter from the moment of birth. Others will be useless or even dangerous in relation to the reality of his present environment. For example, the instinct of prehistoric man to wield a club or stone ax to kill wild animals for food may be applicable in some remote, uncivilized tribes today, but in relation to our own urban civilization it is impractical and unrealistic. The energy expended in the instinctive search for food has to be redirected into acceptable channels, such as working at a job or profession.

The conscious mind serves as a monitor between the inner world of instinctual energies and the external world of present reality. Its function is to receive stimulation or energy from both sources, to correlate these energies, select the correct channel, and discharge the combined energies in the form of realistic behavior. For example, when the body becomes dehydrated, a center in the brain stimulates the conscious mind to awareness of this condition. It allows the thirst instinct to enter from the subconscious and receives external information through sight as to an available source of water—drinking fountain, faucet, water cooler, etc. Correlating these stimuli, the conscious mind directs the proper muscles in appropriate action to drink the water and satisfy the body's need.

The job of the conscious mind is not always so simple. It must hold back or repress undesirable energies entering it that would be dangerous to the survival of the individual in present reality. Once such instinctual energies enter the conscious mind, they must be discharged or intolerable tensions will build up—for the mental apparatus, too, is subject to the law of inertia, and seeks equilibrium. When we say we are "all steamed up" and need to "cool off," we are applying this law to ourselves in the same terms as it applies to water. Water is converted into steam only when it is brought to a boiling point. It returns to its original calm, inactive state as soon as the temperature is reduced sufficiently.

In the human, the conscious mind must, as quickly as possible, reduce the temperature of "boiling" instinctual energies by redirecting them from destructive into constructive channels—like using steam to pull a train. For example, anger aroused by an argument can be released by going out to the golf course and hitting a ball with a club instead of clubbing the opponent on the head as a prehistoric ancestor would have done. Acts and crimes of violence occur when the conscious mind is not strong enough to control and redirect the primitive instinctual energies —such as when the boiler bursts in a steam plant.

Although civilized man has devised codes of behavior for community living, such behavior patterns are too recent in evolutionary time to have become instincts. A child is taught through family, church, and society to sublimate raw, instinctual energies. If he is correctly trained, his conscious mind soon learns that acceptable behavior is more pleasant than primitive gratification. Through such acquired knowledge, the individual makes adaptations for survival in the community of his fellows. If civilization as we know it continues long enough, no doubt some of these adaptations will become instinctive.

So far we have been discussing the instincts which perpetuate the individual organism until it reaches death by completing the natural life cycle of its species.

What about the life instincts, the innate compulsion for immortality? We know that the mental apparatus is immortal. How is it perpetuated?

Immortality cannot be achieved alone. It results from the renewal of life by the fusion of two cells into one. It is thus that the mental apparatus has been and continues to be transmitted and perpetuated from the beginning of life to this very second. By this means we live on, not only through our children but in all life—past, present, and future—not as a dream or a memory but as a physical and mental fact.

This instinct for renewal of life through fusion with another is called libido. The libidinal instincts are governed by the natural law of reproduction. Their basic purpose is the perpetuation of the individual organism for posterity.

The record of accumulated instinctual energies from the beginning of life through those of the particular species is transmitted through the fusion of the male and female cells. It is these germ cells that are immortal. In multicellular forms of life, the germ cells have an existence separate from the rest of the organism. They are in it but not of it. While the rest of the organism instinctively seeks the peace of death, the function of the germ cells is to continue the eternal stream of life.

These libidinal instincts are the basis of human sexuality. Their physical part, however, is only one phase. Although the fusion of the human sperm and ovum has the same fundamental purpose as that of simple one-celled organisms, the human process is as different from the unicellular as calculus is from simple arithmetic. During the millions of years of human evolution a whole complex of new instincts connected with libido, or sexuality, has developed.

Today the mental aspect of human sexuality has become as important as the physical. There must be fusion of minds as well as bodies. Without mental union, physical union is always incomplete and frequently impossible. When a man and woman fulfill each other's mental and emotional needs, the sex act becomes the intimate expression of their love. They feel completely united, not only with each other but with all life. The result is such a full release of all tensions and energies at the climax that a state of Freudian pleasure is temporarily achieved, plus the joy of sharing this complete relaxation with another—the acme of human bliss.

XII

∽∽∽∽∽∽∽∽∽∽∽∽∽∽∽∽∽∽∽∽∽∽∽∽∽

Love—Hate

Man comes into the world with fists clenched, and
leaves with palms open.

The relative strength of these life instincts versus the
death instincts determines the individual's "will to live" or
"will to die." Medical annals and my own experience record
cases of the same illness—under similar circumstances and
treatment—from which one patient recovered while another
one died. In the first case the life instincts were stronger and
opposed the effects of the illness in interfering with life; in the
second the death instincts predominated and joined the forces
of disease to return the patient to an effortless state.

As noted in Chapter 11, the human mental apparatus consists of two parts: the conscious and the subconscious. The
conscious mind's operation might be likened to that of a
supercomputer. From the subconscious, it receives stored
instinctual knowledge and energies. From the physical sensory organs of touch, taste, sight, smell, and hearing, it receives information from the external world. The conscious
mind must be selective in the type of energy it admits from
each source. Just as we close our eyes against a blinding light
or stop our ears against a deafening noise, our consciousness

blocks the admission of instinctual energies that would be dangerous to survival in our present environment. If objectionable energies force their way through, the conscious mind seeks to convert them into acceptable forms. In so doing, for example, love may turn to hate or hate to love.

Once energy has been admitted to the conscious mind, however, it must be discharged in some type of behavior. Normally, when the conscious mind "matches" instinctual and external energies, it joins or binds them together, and discharges them through three main channels (see diagram).

Diagram of Mind

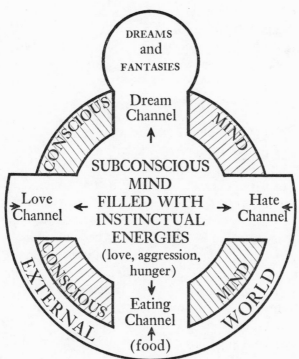

Energies entering the conscious mind may use any or all channels for escape. To avoid tension from unreleased energies, channels may be used that seem inappropriate for a need. Desires that cannot be vented satisfactorily into the external world of reality may find relief in the world of dreams.

Dreams are natural safety valves for satisfying forbidden desires. Sometimes the wish-fulfillment in dreams is obvious and easily traced to the real desire. More often, however, the wish is disguised to make it more acceptable to the ego and conscience. Behavior that would threaten the individual if acted upon in real life (as in the Oedipus dreams previously discussed) can be safely released in dreams. Dreams are usually quickly forgotten, and no guilt feelings should be attached to them. They should provide a sense of well-being. If the mind cannot discharge conscious energies into reality or dreams, the frustrations are turned inward, causing various degrees of depression and self-destruction.

Love Turned into Hunger

To the infant, eating is almost synonymous with love. As the baby drinks from its mother's breast, the flow of milk that satisfies hunger is accompanied by the flow of affectionate love between mother and child. This double pleasure (sensual and compassionate) is associated with excitations from the lips and sucking. That is why the kiss persists throughout life as an expression of love. It is also the subconscious source of the affectionate declaration, "I could just eat you up!" The infant, male or female, wants to possess the mother completely—to consume this source of physical and emotional nourishment. Although there is no thought of physically eating the loved objects, the oral individual symbolically wants to consume them both mentally and physically. When an oral individual loses a love object, he finds it difficult to transfer the invested love to another person. The love energy snaps back into himself. If the retained love cannot be released into the external world through other channels, it may be used for self-pity or melancholia. Frequency, this love is redirected through the eating channel and causes obesity.

Mrs. O is twenty-nine years of age and is seventy-six pounds overweight. She has had two unhappy marriages that have ended in divorce. She goes from one doctor and diet to another without success. Her excuses for not being able to reduce run like this:

> "The diet may work on others, but it doesn't work for me."
> "I haven't eaten a thing, and I gain weight."
> "You have overlooked a glandular problem."
> "You have overlooked a hereditary problem."
> "I'll do anything to lose, Doctor, if *you'll* help me."

As the firstborn of several children, Mrs. O was the center of her parents' affectionate care for five or six years. She had a consuming love for her mother and father. When the family increased and younger children received their share of parental attention, she deeply resented these intruders for whom, she felt, her parents had abandoned her. At first she was unable to vent her love for her parents through the love channel and directed it into the hate channel, resulting in hostility for her younger brothers or sisters. When she was punished for such actions, the aggressive channel became cemented along with the blocked love channel. Still needing to express her love instincts and wanting her parents' attention, she discovered that they were concerned about her eating. As she continued to use this channel to win their approval, she completely regressed to the oral stage of emotional development. In addition, the love and hate energies redirected through the eating channel became eroticized with the pleasure of eating and became a means of sensual gratification.

Under these circumstances, Mrs. O's Electra complex could

not resolve itself naturally. Her feeling of being rejected by her parents gave her a sense of inferiority, of being unworthy of receiving love from anyone. Her blueprint for love was designed from her experiences with members of her family and made her incapable of loving anyone. With her love channel blocked in both directions, she could not make a successful adjustment in marriage. Since her hate channel was also blocked from early experiences, she could not openly express her subconcious hostility toward the Electra substitute, her husband. Her tensions and frustrations were so strong that they could find only partial release in dreams.

Eating, therefore, has become Mrs. O's only channel for expressing love and hate. The intake of food and its passage through her lips has a sensuous, erotic meaning which substitutes for mature sexuality. She also gobbles her food down fast, finding in the vigorous cutting, biting, and chewing of her food a release of her aggressive energies.

Whenever she tries to diet, some of these energies force their way back through the aggressive channel for release, and Mrs. O becomes cantankerous and irritable. She is unable to release enough aggressiveness through this channel, however, and she gets "so nervous" that she compulsively abandons her diet and once more eats excessively. Or if she continues her diet for a longer period, and forces more energy through the aggressive channel, the destructive energies formed turn inward against herself. As a result, she becomes depressed, even to the point of contemplating suicide.

Unaware of these subconscious motivations—or, if made aware of them, fearful of their exposure—Mrs. O must "eat or die"; so she eats herself into a slow death.

Sometimes men can handle overweight problems much better than women because, even though the love channel becomes blocked, they can more easily replace eating pleasures with the sex act. In men, too, blocked love and hunger needs are more easily diverted into aggressive channels. All athletic activities, for example, are a means of releasing natural aggressive energy. When diverted love energy is added to aggressiveness, it can lead to outstanding achievement in competitive sports. Love of the game encourages professionalism.

Love Turned into Hate

Mr. G was such a case. One of seven children, he received no love and very little food from his indigent, alcoholic parents. Sleep provided some outlet in dreams but since there was never enough food available, love and hunger needs could not be directed through the eating channel. These feelings were mainly diverted into aggressiveness. At school he was constantly fighting with other students and was expelled. He ran away from home and became a tramp. His over-aggressiveness could easily have led him into a life of crime, but, fortunately, boxing promoters took an interest in the young scrapper and trained him as a professional fighter.

Mr. G's love channel was so blocked up that he could never love a woman, and he told me that he never had loved one. Love and hate urges were released in the boxing ring, and he fought his way up to become a contender for an international championship.

Beaten in this contest, Mr. G retired to live like a hermit in the Western mountains. He used his aggression to hunt and fish and to overcome a hostile environment. After several years he developed tuberculosis and was hospitalized. The confinement provided no way to release aggressiveness. He became severely depressed and was transferred to the psychiatric ward.

Hate Turned to Love

Conversely, repressed aggressive energies may become diverted into the love channels where they are released in the form of overly courteous, submissive, and solicitous behavior. Recent sensational cases of model young men who

Sex and Sanity

suddenly become killers illustrate this type—such as Duane Pope, star athlete and honor student, who two days after his college graduation robbed a bank and killed three people; and Charles Whitman, dutiful son and steady husband, who killed his wife and mother and then went on a shooting spree at the University of Texas. Both were described as the "All-American Boy" type—handsome, courteous, with "never a cross word for anyone." Mothers pointed to them as models of behavior for their sons. On the witness stand, Pope reverted to his former mild, calm manner while he revealed violent waking fantasies—not dreams—that had haunted him all his life and which finally broke through into "uncontrollable" action. Whitman told of his lifelong hatred of his father —a vindictive disciplinarian who beat his wife and son. Yet perversely the son subconsciously identified with his father as the symbol of adult power, and this—added to an unresolved Oedipus complex—caused his repressed love and hate to explode through the hate channel against his mother and mother substitute, then on to the murder of other women.

The repression of natural aggressiveness into overpoliteness can characterize an entire society, as with the Japanese prior to World War II. The dense population of this island nation made it essential, for mutual survival, for the people to repress all normal destructive instincts to an extreme degree. So strong was this conscious barrier that when aggressive energies became overwhelming, the Japanese citizen turned the destructive force against himself and committed hara-kiri.

However, when an end to the nation's isolation came and it was presented with a foreign "hate object," the repressed aggressive energies of centuries blasted through the cemented hate channel, and peaceful Japan turned into a fanatic aggressor. The atrocities committed by Japanese soldiers, the banzai charges and kamikaze attacks—unique in the history of warfare—were products of this national explosion of pent-up hate energies.

The fanaticism of the German Nazis was of a different

type. From German tradition it contained an element of repressed aggression which—under the extreme discipline of absolute authority—released itself individually in good manners and cold intellect, and nationally in warlike aggression and the humiliation of other peoples. Their esteem for themselves led to delusions of grandeur in the doctrine of the *ubermensch* (superman). Hitler, an extreme paranoiac himself, provided the spark which released their pent-up hostilities in the form of a national paranoia.

A mild form of paranoia is sometimes observed in normal human society. It is evident in people who release their aggressive energies by constantly complaining about their neighbors, spreading rumors and malicious gossip. As long as it does not become excessive, it can be tolerated.

XIII

〰〰〰〰〰〰〰〰〰〰〰〰〰〰〰〰〰〰〰

The Essential Ingredient

What is the essential ingredient of human sexuality?

It is what every human being longs for—to find the answer to one's innermost needs and desires in complete union with another. The answer is not that one plus one equals two, but that one-half plus one-half equals one. It is finding the other half of oneself.

In unicellular organisms this complete union is achieved chemically. Each has been depleted by continuous fission, and seeks to merge with another of its kind for a mutual renewal of life. The fusion of the infinitely more complex male and female germ cells of the human reenacts this primal process—but it does not of itself achieve the union of man and woman. This demands far more than simple chemistry.

When a man or a woman speaks of a spouse as "my better half," the reference is not to a mere sex partner, but to a partner in all the aspects of personal life.

The concept of a man and woman as two halves of a single entity is found in the legends and religions of mankind from earliest times. According to Greek mythology, for example, the first human creature had two heads, four arms, four legs, and both male and female genitalia. Zeus cut this creature in two, one-half becoming man and the other half woman. Ever since, these two halves have sought to reunite.* In Hindu legend, the Creator made man out of the stronger elements of nature, using the more ethereal elements to fashion woman —the two thus complementing each other to form a natural union. In the Judeo-Christian Bible story (Genesis 2:23–24), God took a rib from man to create woman:

And Adam said, This is now bone of my bones, and flesh of my flesh; she shall be called Woman, because she was taken out of Man. Therefore shall a man leave his father and his mother, and shall cleave unto his wife: and they shall be one flesh.

Each is incomplete without the other. The essence of loneliness—which may be one of man's earliest instincts—is this sense of incompleteness. It is a loneliness that can only find peace in the perfect union of man and woman.

The key to this complete union—the essential ingredient—is also part of inherent human wisdom, as expressed in legend and religion. The stories of creation in various cultures throughout the world follow a similar pattern. First the earth from the emptiness of space, then the separation of the land from the sea, the day from the night. Next the creation of plants, followed by fish, birds, and animals of all kinds. Finally man, who was given dominion over the earth and all its creatures. In spite of his power and prestige, however, man was lonely. And so—not primarily for the purpose of procreation —but to fill this loneliness, woman was created. As the Bible story told it in Genesis 2:18:

Then the Lord God said, It is not good that the man should be alone. I will make him a helpmate fit for him.

The key word—the essential ingredient—is *helpmate*. It is to this helpmate that a man cleaves "and they become one." This key word is still included in most marriage ceremonies,

* Plato, in his *Symposium*, theorizes that the force separating man and woman sets up a counterforce—loneliness, a longing for the other half.

and if it were always taken seriously and thoughtfully there would be many more happy marriages and many fewer divorces.

Helpmate means just what it says—to help one's mate. To each partner, the other's welfare and happiness comes first. To help each other is the primary consideration. When the helpmate quality is present, the other desirable qualities develop—compatibility, companionship, mutual interests, understanding, and deep affection. Good looks and money are not essential. If a man thinks his wife is beautiful, she becomes so. The inner beauty of loving and being loved shines through even the homeliest features. If a woman thinks her husband is intelligent, he develops capacities of intelligence and achievement that he would not have dreamed possible.

The helpmate quality is the answer to the frequently asked question, "Why did he marry her?" or "Why did she marry him?" He finds in her the perfect helpmate, who lovingly understands his needs and considers that fulfilling them is the most important thing in the world. He reciprocates by wanting, above all else, to make her happy. She finds in him the fulfillment of woman's primary need, the assurance that she is the most important person in the world to her man. Their mental embrace is so complete that their intimate physical embrace in the sex act becomes an ecstasy of union expressing their love.

These fortunate people never have to justify to anyone their choice of each other. They radiate the answer. Those who question, "What does one see in the other?" reveal a subconscious envy.

Such a complete relationship can seldom, if ever, exist outside of marriage. Marriage provides the openly recognized symbol that each partner puts the welfare and happiness of the other above all else.

Even long-lasting common-law marriages, which apparently include the essential ingredient, are incomplete. The woman in particular needs both the symbolism and the practical protection of legal marriage. I have had quite a few patients who were common-law man and wife, and who seemed to be very happy. All too often, however, when the man died his inheritance went to his children by a former legal marriage, and the woman who had shared his later life as a true help-mate was left destitute. Instances are cited of common-law marriages which were happy until they were legalized, then emotional problems developed. From my clinical experience, I would say that the emotional maladjustment existed before-hand in one or both partners in an unresolved Oedipus or Electra complex, making the abnormal unwed state seem normal—as in the case of Julia in Chapter 10. Such unfortunate people, who are incomplete in themselves, cannot achieve complete union with another.

The marriage ceremony is by no means a magic formula that insures wedded bliss. The married status may be mis-used for ulterior motives such as gaining wealth or position, or for other expedient purposes. It may be entered into be-cause of family pressures, an unexpected pregnancy, or the excitement of temporary physical attraction. Such marriages seldom endure—or if they do, the price is misery for one or both partners.

A happy marriage requires constant effort, even by two people who love each other deeply and have entered into the marriage contract sincerely. Take Patty and Bob's case, for example. As discussed in Chapter 2, they had to learn to understand each other fully before they could become real helpmates. Because of their genuine affection and desire to help each other, they were able to reconcile the differences in their physical sex drives and to grow up together toward a rewarding maturity and completeness in their married life.

Even well-intentioned marriages can fail to develop into a united partnership. The stumbling blocks are small at first, but unless they are removed, molehills can grow into moun-tains. Dissatisfactions and disappointments are seldom voiced directly by either the husband or the wife. Expression usually

takes the form of nagging about little things, which are subconscious symbols of the main issue. The husband, for instance, will criticize his wife about her housekeeping, her
absence because she is at a bridge party or PTA meeting when
he comes home. To him, her attention to the home and his
needs symbolizes her love for him. She, in turn, will feel
aggrieved if he forgets her birthday or their anniversary,
neglects to kiss her good-bye, or fails to admire her new dress.
To her, the small acts are symbolic of his love for her.
Each subconsciously feels that the other should know and
understand, without being told, that the real meaning behind
the nagging is a signal of the need for loving reassurance.

It takes a discerning helpmate to recognize and interpret
these signals, and tactfully correct the situation. All too often
the small affronts to each other's ego are suffered in silence
until they build up into an explosive argument. Afterward,
when husband and wife go to bed, the comfort of physical
touch may bring about a reconciliation culminating in intercourse. If this pattern is repeated too often, however, the wife
comes to resent it. She feels that she is merely being used
physically by her husband, and retaliates by refusing to
cooperate in the sex act. He then becomes convinced that
she does not love him. In an attempt to ease his own hurt by
hurting her, he may resort to adultery, or subconsciously
revenge himself by some form of psychological impotence.

Among my patients, for example, were a likeable henpecked
husband and his domineering wife, whom he apparently
adored because of her beauty and intellect. It was a real
Oedipus substitution for both of them, for the parents of
both the husband and the wife had had the same pattern
of a domineering female and a henpecked male.

This couple had been married seven years and had two
talented children. Although the wife was really very fond of
her husband, she did not know how to be a helpmate. Her
interests always came first, and every decision had to have
her stamp of approval. A quiet man, her husband did not

openly rebel. Finally, however, the years of pent-up sub-conscious resentment—in childhood against his mother and in marriage against his wife—demanded release. His instinct for self-determination exploded in premature ejaculation—having an orgasm just before performance of the sex act. Up to this time, this couple's physical sex life had been quite satis-factory. Neither of them realized what had suddenly gone wrong. Characteristically the husband was too embarrassed to speak to me about this inability to have normal sex rela-tions, but his wife asked my advice.

During several consultations with them both, the situation was analyzed. When the husband realized that his impotence was a mental problem, he was able to overcome it and resume normal relationships. His wife, however, was unable to make the necessary adjustment. Having been indoctrinated since infancy with the superiority of women, she could not stop bossing her husband. He did not return to impotence, but sub-consciously resorted to other means of asserting his repressed instincts of mastery and self-determination. He started drink-ing and lost his job.

Unless psychiatric treatment can help these people become better adjusted to themselves and to each other, the only salvation for this couple is divorce. The basic causes of their marital troubles remain unsolved, despite the resumption of normal sex relations.

The sex act is not the essential ingredient. Without it the union between man and woman is incomplete, but the mar-riage can endure as long as the helpmate quality is present. Without this essential ingredient, however—regardless of geni-tal sex relations—the marriage partnership tends to become mutually destructive and should be dissolved. A man and woman who are forced to share an empty life develop a marital malignancy that is harmful to them and to others. Marriage without some gratification for the affectionate and/ or sensual human needs has no purpose in existing.

Men who divorce their wives to marry their secretaries

are often considered heartless. However, an examination of such cases usually reveals that the wife has either failed or ceased to be her husband's helpmate. The secretary fills this basic need. For an equally natural reason, a woman may leave the husband who is a good, steady provider but neglects her as an individual.

Money or the lack of it is often used as the scapegoat to blame for the disintegration of a marriage. When the essential ingredient is present, this is not a factor. Some of the deepest loves are found among couples who have to struggle for a living, because survival depends upon their helping each other. Wealth does not preclude such love, either, as long as the husband and wife remain helpmates in spite of the distractions which money makes possible. When one-half plus one-half equals one, it cannot be split by outside circumstances.

Even in societies that practice polygamy, there is the search for this complete union. By custom and tradition the sultan or chieftain is led to believe that he has a good thing going sexwise by having a harem, and the women have learned to tolerate the situation. But there is always the "favorite wife," the helpmate who shares with her lord and master the essential ingredient of human sexuality. The fabled Scheherezade, for instance, diverted the sultan from the rest of his harem for a thousand and one nights by entertaining him with imaginative stories and thus became his queen. King Solomon is famed in biblical history for his hundreds of wives and concubines. But the Queen of Sheba, who sought the king for his wisdom, was the inspiration for the Song of Songs (or Song of Solomon), one of the most beautiful and sensuous love poems of all time.

In countries where polygamy is practiced today, there is a growing movement toward monogamy, sparked by the infectious new independence of woman in other parts of the world. When the change does come, it will no doubt be explosive, as these women assert their long-repressed instincts for mastery and self-determination.

Although monogamy has been the established custom for centuries in our Western civilizations, the explosion of female independence continues to gain momentum. It is constantly being given new impetus, as mental strength becomes a more important factor than physical strength in human evolution. In her abreaction, however, the modern woman often carries her independence to the point of resenting her natural role of helpmate to man.

There is no subservience implied in the status of helpmate. Rather it is a tribute to woman that she is the one who must initiate and maintain this relationship with man. This natural state of affairs becomes evident early in the courtship. The man is primarily motivated by his mating instinct. It is the woman who calls attention to the areas of mutual interest, first by adapting her interests to those of the man, then gradually arousing his in matters of her own sphere. From the start she finds pleasure in pleasing and becoming important to him, and this engenders a like response on his part.

Throughout life, it is the woman who remains the hub of the marriage and the home, as Anne Morrow Lindbergh pointed out so eloquently in *Gift from the Sea*. It is from the wife and mother that the spokes of family life radiate. It is she who is the center on which the wheel turns. Even though she may work at a job or career of her own, this helpmate responsibility is still hers. To resent it is a foolish and futile waste of energy. Let it be accepted as a trust.

Being a helpmate is not a passive job. It requires active and sensitive participation by both husband and wife. To realize their full potential as individuals, as well as partners, each needs the other's sincere help. The wife is not expected to believe that her man can do no wrong, and he is not expected to consider her perfect. Criticism does not need to be withheld, but it should be given in a kindly and constructive maner, in a spirit of mutual helpfulness. As one happily married man put it,

It isn't just my inadequacies I can let out in front of my wife. It's my successes as well. . . . This kind of relationship is really only possible between a man and a woman. I don't want to boast of my achievements even to my childhood buddy, and I certainly don't want to confess my weaknesses to him. Bald or not, a man has to let his hair down sometime. And for that he needs a wife.*

To a man, his home and his work are paramount. To a woman, her husband and her home must come first. She may be active in a bridge club, the PTA, politics, or other interests —but these must be kept secondary. As the hub of the home, her rewards may not be measured as tangibly as a man's in his sphere, but they are just as real. By nature, a woman's need is to give. Her real happiness depends upon the happiness she gives to her husband and their children.

The distinction is important—her husband and their children. The complete union between husband and wife is cemented by the essential ingredient, the helpmate quality. They share their love with their children, who are the result of this union, but they must not rob each other to do so. The wife who forgets this and expends all her helpmate quality on her children returns to her initial loneliness when they leave. She may or may not be able to reunite with her husband. This is frequently the cause of depression in middle age, when a woman should really be in the flower of her life. The wise woman remembers that, in the usual course of events, she and her husband will be living with each other long after their children are grown and building their own lives. A man needs a helpmate all his life.

The analogy of the pack horse, as noted in Chapter 4, applies here as well. By nature, man is as reluctant as the pack horse to carry his load up and down the winding trail of life. But like the pack horse, he responds to a skillful wrangler, who knows how to distribute and tie down the pack load

* James Lincoln Collins, "When a Man Marries," *Reader's Digest*, October, 1966.

properly so it will be the least burdensome. When he balks
on the trail or tries to shake off the load, even the most
"onery critter" can be pacified and prodded on his way by
expert handling. As Henry Wadsworth Longfellow in "The
Song of Hiawatha" put it,

> As unto the bow the cord is,
> So unto the man is woman.
> Though she bends him, she obeys him,
> Though she draws him, yet she follows,
> Useless each without the other!

When one of the partners of a complete union dies, the
other partner usually follows soon—or remarries soon. The
loss of one's other half is too much to be borne. Contrary
to the unthinking general opinion of society, such a remarriage is a tribute to, not a reflection on, the former spouse.
Mr. J, a patient of mine, was in this category. He and his
wife had been wonderfully happy together. When she died,
he felt like only half a person. How he found another woman
with as much life as his former wife, I do not know, but find
her he did, and married her within three months after the
first Mrs. J's death. Many people in the community were
shocked. They failed to realize that Mr. J's desperate need for
a helpmate like his former wife was an eloquent proof of
his love for her.

As for a widow who has been a true helpmate, she possesses
the world's best weapon for the conquest of man. Above all
else—regardless of age, appearance, or affluence—the magnet
that draws a man is the helpmate quality. It is the essential
ingredient for human happiness.

XIV

~~~~~~

Male and Female Responses

When my wife and I were visiting San Francisco, some friends there arranged to show us the city's night life. At the well-known North Beach area, we dropped into a large cabaret. A topless contest was just getting under way. The audience was composed mostly of college students, the ratio of men to women about two to one. The young MC was announcing the five volunteers competing for the first prize in topless performance.

These young women were not, as might be supposed, illiterate or semidelinquents. One was an entymologist, another an airline hostess, and three were instructors—in judo, in trampoline, and in swimming at the YWCA. The only show of modesty which any of the girls exhibited was at the moment each stepped behind the curtain to remove her blouse. Then, to blaring African music, she swung onto the stage and went into an unrestrained frenzy of flailing her breasts in rhythm with the savage beat of the orchestra.

The topless young women were so unrepressed and unconcerned about exhibiting their writhing torsos that the audience seemed blasé and indifferent to their demonstrations. The contestants were obviously flaunting their nakedness as an assertion of female mastery in flouting a taboo and not for artistic expression.

Burlesque queens, go-go artists, and topless-bottomless professionals whose contortions are deliberately provocative are as a rule sexually cold for the sex act. In addition, some of them delight in arousing men's sexual desire, then leaving them in a state of unrelieved tension—a subtle subconscious revenge for the thousands of years that women were held in subjugation by men.

How can the female of the human species—from teen-ager to topless performer to motion-picture star—appear so sexy and yet remain indifferent and even frigid in her attitude toward the sex act?

Granted that many women of all ages indulge in sexual intercourse and that a minority of them are repulsed by it and that still another minority have an unusually strong sex drive, the fact remains that nature has equipped the average human male with a more intense sex drive than even the sexiest female. Women appear more sexy because of their mannerisms and gestures. These activities, which seem so provocative, actually serve to release some of their sensual sex tensions without meaning that they wish to engage in the sex act with the men observing them.

A woman has many more intense erotic zones on her body than a man does. Erotically stimulating sensations for the normal male are concentrated in his penis. But in the female, sensations are more scattered—her strongest excitations remain in the genital area, but her breasts, lips, neck, thighs, and other parts of her body are also sensually excitable. Vaginal sensations in the female cannot be compared with the pressure of the male organ; the sensual excitations in women cannot always be exactly localized. Female sensual sex is like a shotgun shell, scattering in all directions, while the male's is like a rifle shot, making a direct hit.

In infancy and early childhood, the boy's attention is drawn to the penile organ by anything that stimulates it. Pressure of the thighs, urinating, and scratching may cause excitement in this structure. He soon learns that the tension produced by such irritations can be relieved by further rubbing or stroking his penis. Then he discovers that beyond relieving these irritations, the mechanical stimuli can produce pleasurable excitations. From infancy the male becomes conditioned to regarding and using his penis as the primary anatomical center of excitation for sensual pleasure.

Since these penis-centered lust feelings are part of his Oedipus complex toward his mother (Chapter 7), and thus carry with them a subconscious sense of guilt, the little boy subconsciously misinterprets punishment as due to his "sinful" incestual desires. He fears that the ultimate punishment may involve cutting off the anatomical source of his lust, the penis. These hidden fears—known as the castration complex—are intensified when punishment or criticism comes from his mother, especially when it is in connection with bedwetting, urinating in improper places, showing off his penis (as all male children are prone to do), or other such matters related to his genitals.

The first experience of having to go to school is often subconsciously misinterpreted as rejection by the loved parent. He frequently rebels in stormy, tearful scenes and, when forced to stay, may run back home at the first opportunity. Separation from the loved parent, and from objects in the home, such as food, which helps satisfy pleasurable desires, is subconsciously feared by the child as an indication that the parent is abandoning and punishing him for his lust feelings.*

Similar reactions may occur in connection with the first haircut, going to the dentist, or going to the hospital, especially to have the tonsils removed. I have always been very careful to explain to children exactly what an operation or treatment involves, why it is necessary, and how it is done. Such information, I believe, is absolutely essential before

* Children who learn to rely on food as an acceptable sensuous pleasure approved by the parent or which attracts the parent's attention may become quite obese. Efforts to reduce fail, for dieting interferes with the child's sensual adjustments.

performing a tonsilectomy. Failure to allay the child's sub-conscious fears may lead to serious emotional disturbances.

In little girls, the infantile castration complex soon disap-pears and is replaced by "penis envy." When children dis-cover the difference in genital anatomy between the two sexes, little boys and little girls both subconsciously assume that the little girl has already been castrated. The boy feels superior and the girl envies him, but she quickly learns to accept herself anatomically and normally becomes indifferent to the comparison. Instead of having one central focus of sensuality, she finds out that many parts of her body respond pleasurably to stimulations. This sensation may first occur in her clitoris, the tiny remnant of a penis just above the vaginal opening, but mechanically stimulating it does not usually relieve all her subconscious sexual needs. The partial relief, in fact, may produce nervousness and she may develop an aversion to touching the clitoris.

This is why masturbation, which is common in boys of three to five years and after puberty, is not as common in girls (except when the clitoris is an unusually sensitive erotic zone). Relief of female sex energies often results from playing with other parts of the genitals such as the labia or "lips" that cover the vaginal opening, the vaginal walls, or the cervix (the mouth of the uterus inside the vagina), or from fondling the breasts, squeezing the buttocks, or moving the lips and mouth in actions such as thumb sucking or kissing. In older girls and women, the putting on of undergarments and hose may involve subconscious caresses that excite and release some sexual tension.

Although it is not analyzed or consciously recognized, the sensual need for touch and self-caress in women is intuitively understood and accepted in our society. For example, it would be considered shockingly odd to portray a man with sensually puckered lips on a billboard advertising the pleasures of drinking "X Beer." But it is perfectly acceptable to show a women whose lips are sensually pursed for a kiss. The male exhibitionist is regarded with disgust, but the female figure is hailed as "the form divine," whenever or however displayed. Swinging the hips and other movements of the female body also produce sensuous excitations. Marilyn Monroe engaged in such various sensuous activities while satisfying, via the fantasy route, a multitude of male screen viewers. The eroticism of her entire body, and its misinterpretation by herself and others as an intense sex drive, could well have been the main cause of unhappiness in her personal sex life. Most women satiating their physical sex needs by using the numerous erotic parts of their bodies are usually unrequited with the mature genital sex act.

It is the scattered "shotgun" nature of female sexuality manifested in our everyday environment which gives the false impression of the sexiness of women. Since the male's "rifle shot" sex drive is aimed at one target—sexual intercourse—it is mistakenly assumed that this is also the primary female goal. It isn't.

The preliminary lovemaking, which only stimulates the intensity of male desire, actually releases much of the female's sexual tensions and makes it unnecessary for her to rely solely on the sex act. Many misguided males, advised by sexperts in how to overcome the female's resistance to the sex act, attempt to stimulate excessively their companion's erotic zones. In so doing they dissipate the sensual needs of the female and may make her less dependent on genital gratification.

Some women, whose genital organs do not act as a primary source of sensual excitations, prefer a "good lover" to a mature man. These women have numerous highly intense erotic zones without a main central one. They are prone to have promiscuous affairs or become prostitutes, not because they are "sex mad" for intercourse but because the average man, oriented to the sex act, does not satisfy all their various erotic needs. In having affairs with many men, one may be more capable of satisfying their vaginal erotic zones, another their visual excitations and exhibitionistic drives, still another their oral needs, and so on. In this way, prostitution helps them come in contact with enough men having various sexual needs to satisfy their own.

As noted, infants and children derive a subconscious sexual satisfaction from learning about the body and its functions and about birth. This early sensual pleasure associated with the acquisition of knowledge remains in some degree throughout life. Many adults sublimate part or a great deal of their libidinal energies in study or research or in acquiring new skills. Women especially find a certain sexual gratification in the company of intellectual men—for example, consider the popularity of male authors and lecturers at women's clubs.

There is often a subconscious sexual response to "faith healers" who exploit the sensuality of touch. The "laying on of hands" relieves tensions in neurotic individuals, whose "cures" result from the pleasurable relaxation upon such release. Even in the legitimate practice of medicine, this principle must be applied to a certain extent, because many patients feel dissatisfied if the physician does not actually touch and examine the painful part of the body. Mrs. J, for example, left her doctor because he did not actually put his hand on her head to "feel" her headache though he had taken her history and given her a complete physical examination. She believed that it was necessary to touch the affected part to make a diagnosis.

Discomfort is relieved by mineral and sauna baths, massage, and similar therapy—not because of the minerals and ointments, but because the warmth and contact arouse a sensuous response in the skin, dissipating tension and producing a feeling of pleasure. This mental release in turn relaxes tight, tense muscles, relieving their pressure on the joints or other damaged bodily structures, and the pain subsides. Treatment at some spas includes not only bathing in the springs, but also drinking the hot mineral water. The laxative effect stimulates bowel movements which produce a sensation of pleasure associated with infancy. Experiences in life from the relationship with parents and friends, the entertainment media, and the social attitudes, all affect the sexual growth of the child. When these are conducive to normal development, the individual becomes a sexually mature adult whose maximum sexual pleasure is achieved from the genital sex acts, although remnants of earlier stages provide some residual excitations. Abnormal and harmful sexual experiences, especially among young people, lead to arrested sexuality, or perversions.

XV

~~~~~~~~~~~~~~~~~~~~~~~~~~~~~~~~~~~~

The Anatomy of the Sex Act

A Frenchman and a Englishman were discussing the sex act. "There are thirty positions," declared the Frenchman with a superior air.

"I beg your pardon," corrected the Englishman. "There are thirty-one." Indignant that an Englishman should presume to know more about the art of sexual intercourse than a Frenchman, the latter rattled off his thirty positions, then flung a challenging look at his companion.

"Quite," agreed the Englishman blandly. "But then, there is also the normal way."

The natural sex act intimately involving two people of the opposite sex is as natural an event as the sunrise. In such genital relationships there is no normal position—all are normal.

For the average, normal couple the sex act is performed with the woman lying on her back with her thighs spread and the man occupying the position provided. Some partners perfer lying on their sides, facing each other. If the woman's primary erotic zone is the cervix, another position may be necessary for the penis to reach the cervix for maximum stimulation—such as the woman lying face down and the man above her. In some women the instinct for mastery and the rebellion from man's domination are so assertive that the most satisfying method is for the woman to occupy the top position with the man lying on his back.

Some prefer lighted surroundings, others darkness to intensify their gratification. These and other preferences depend on the individual's supportive senses, which give additional excitation. Light excites the sensual impulses for seeing, and dark stimulates the sensual excitement of mystery. The need for kissing, caressing, and fondling are subordinate to the genital urge but help determine what position is most satisfactory for the sex act of a particular individual.

The sex act is the natural result of a mental need that relies upon the physical for its fulfillment. As previously discussed, instinctual energies that create anxiety in the conscious mind are held back in the subconscious mind. These repressed energies accumulate and build up discomforting tension. When pressures become too great from the external world or subconscious sources or both, the conscious mind summons the libidinal instincts to the rescue. The sexual act provides a means of releasing these pent-up instincts and the associated mental tension. The physical excitations arising during sexual intercourse receive energy from the subconscious energies. The excitations bind the repressed instincts and discharge them at the time of the climax and orgasm. The mind, relieved of the built-up mental energies—and in accord with the pleasure principle—feel relieved and at peace.

Both memory and the senses inform the conscious mind of the desired presence of the loved partner, with whom sexual intercourse provides the most complete and pleasurable sexual release. These thoughts automatically stimulate sensuous areas of the body, arousing the desire for further excitation.

In the male, the center of this sensuous reaction is the genitals. Seeing and touching his female partner, or sometimes even only thinking of her, stimulates a physical reflex in this area. The penis is largely composed of erectile tissue, which is a system of blood channels called sinuses.

When the sensory stimulus activates the motor nerves at the base of the spinal column, blood rushes in to fill these empty sinuses, producing an erection—an enlargement and hardening of the organ which makes sexual intercourse possible for the man. From the testes the male sperm migrate through ducts into the prostate gland, which is located inside the body at the base of the bladder. The sperm on reaching the prostate mix with the secretions of this gland and form the semen which is ejaculated at the time of an orgasm.

During sexual intercourse, the movements involving the genital structures of the sex partners develop extreme excitations. When the excitement reaches its peak, muscular contractions force the semen from the prostate into and through the uretha, the channel of the penis. This ejaculation of the male releases both physical and mental tensions in a sex climax or orgasm.

Following the climax, the blood-filled sinuses empty and the penis loses its erection. The male sex partner feels composure with a deep sense of peace and contentment.

In the average female, the genital area provides for a majority of sensual excitations but other erotic zones account for additional excitations (discussed in the previous chapter). These zones vary in different individuals, but as an example let us assume that her major excitable area is the genitals, with subordinate areas in the breasts, skin, and mouth. As her senses are stimulated by the presence of her loved partner, there is an increase in the mucous secretions of the vagina, preparing it for the sex act.

The breasts, which also contain erectile tissue in the nipples, become engorged and the nipples erect. The woman's skin tingles, her mouth becomes moist, and her lips automatically puckered. The caresses of her lover increase the flow of excitation from the breasts and skin, and his kisses increase the excitability of her mouth.

If her excitations reach a sufficient degree and if she mentally desires to love her sex partner, she may reach a climax

and have an orgasm without the sex act. She feels reposed and
further stimulation of her sensuous organs fails to produce
pleasurable excitations. If her sexual act fails to reach a climax,
the incompletely relieved mental tension is disquieting unless
she releases it in the feeling of satisfaction from having loved
and been loved by her partner—that is, unless she converts the
physical needs into affectionate feelings.

The female orgasm consists of an ejaculation of very
slight secretions from small glands located at the entrance
of the vagina, known as Skene's glands, and from the Bartho-
lin glands, whose primary purpose is ʰo keep the vagina
moist. These secretions contain no gᴜ n cells. The female
egg or ovum remains inside the body awaiting fertilization by
the male sperm. During the female sex climax, the muscles at
the entrance of the vagina contract convulsively and in-
voluntarily.

Real satisfaction is enhanced when both partners reach the
climax at the same moment and have simultaneous orgasms.
The average woman, however, has only one or two real
orgasms every month, usually during the time that an egg is
being expelled from an ovary into the uterus. During this
period of several days, when ovum and sperm can unite to
form an embryo, nature intensifies the female sex drive for
the strictly physical purpose of perpetuating the species. At
this time the wife is not only more receptive to her husband's
advances, but may make the first advances toward sexual
intercourse herself. This time of the month varies in individuals, but on the average it occurs about fourteen days after
the start of the menstrual period. Some women have a re-
currence of the desire for genital intercourse just before or
after the menstruation—perhaps to appease a subconscious
longing for pregnancy and anxiety for having missed becoming pregnant at the vulnerable time.

Many women, especially young ones, mistakenly believe
that they experience real, spontaneous orgasms during intercourse because of the pleasure they feel in satisfying a hus-

band or lover. Their satisfactions arise, to a large extent, from a release of affectionate energy during and after the physical union. Until a woman becomes fully matured in her genital sexual experience, she is unaware of the nature of an orgasm.

Many men, not understanding the sex nature of women, feel a sense of frustration or inferiority when their wife or sweetheart fails to respond routinely with an orgasm during every sex act. Since the man always has an orgasm, he believes that he has failed to arouse his partner sufficiently if she does not respond in the same way. If he expresses or shows his disappointment, it is often reflected by his female partner who then feels disappointed for not having pleased him.

Her free flow of affectionate love is impeded by his complaints and she too becomes less satisfied. Both need to be reassured that women do not reach a climax with every sex act and that failure to do so is normal and does not reflect on the sexual abilities of either partner. It is the way nature made the average female and male. When she does not have an orgasm, she must derive her pleasure from affectionate feelings related to loving and pleasing her husband.

If a woman is overly stimulated by preliminary love play in an attempt to arouse her genital feelings, she may release her sexual needs in this way and become less responsive to excitations from her genitals. Such is frequently the unhappy result—for both partners—of using the perverted techniques advocated by the sexperts, who advise getting the girl "turned on by the numbers." Occasionally, if the female organs have been surgically removed, prolonged sex play is beneficial—but it is not so for the average woman.

Sometimes, particularly with newlyweds, the bridegroom is so stimulated, and the bride so eager to please him, that the couple repeatedly indulge in sexual intercourse. The young husband usually comes through physically intact, but the young wife may develop "honeymoon cystitis." The unaccustomed and continuous friction during the sex act irri-

tates and inflames her vagina from which the inflammation
spreads into the urethra (the tube leading from the bladder)
and into the bladder itself, resulting in a severe burning sensation when urinating. This is one of the most common
complaints among young married women. It is also the reason
why women are more subject to kidney infection than men,
because the inflammation spreads from the lower urinary tract
up into the kidneys. This physical complication can produce
psychological complications as well, causing the wife to have
apprehension of later discomfort when engaging in the sex
act. Also emotional disturbances and fears, often brought on
by misinformation or ill-advised suggestions from others, may
cause fear which produces a spasm and tightening of the
vaginal entrance and pain during intercourse. Fear, pain, and
misconceived attitudes regarding the sex act can make the
female frigid.

When a woman is pregnant her interest in the sex act
wanes, but her need for affectionate love increases. This often
complicates matters for some husbands whose desire for sexual intercourse may increase during the wife's pregnancy.
His sensual instinct for knowledge is subconsciously aroused
by the mystery of pregnancy, as well as the innate desire to
do what is forbidden. He may also have new anxieties about
providing for his family, which create more mental tensions
needing relief through intercourse. It is difficult for him to
fulfill his wife's need for affection and at the same time deny
himself fulfillment in the sex act. Normally there is no
physical danger in sexual intercourse during pregnancy, but
the average woman is psychologically disinterested and therefore does not usually enjoy it. In some women pregnancy
increases sexual desires, for they no longer fear becoming
pregnant.

At the other extreme is the woman who feels no affection
for her male partner, but merely regards him as a means of
satisfying her need to release tensions in the sex act. This exceptional type strives to have an orgasm with every act of

sexual intercourse. She learns to contract the vaginal muscles voluntarily, producing a type of pseudo orgasm that is proclaimed by the free-love sexperts. She requires a lover who can sustain or repeat the sex act until she reaches a climax. The average male cannot satisfy her. Her ideal partner is a man whose mental anxieties and feeling of insecurity are so excessive that his conscious mind cannot cope with them without resorting to frequent use of the sex act to discharge them. Such a lover is no sex superman. He merely has an even greater need for release of tensions through sexual intercourse than do other, less anxious men.

These people, who perform the sex act naturally, may be exceptional in their frequent need of it, but they are not abnormal.

There is no normality or abnormality in the human need to release tensions in an orgasm achieved during natural sexual intercourse between male and female. The peace or pleasure that results from this emptying out of tensions is healthful and beneficial. It rejuvenates the mental apparatus, so that it can again cope with the problems of life. As problems build up again they create stresses whose energies must be discharged—and again intercourse may serve this purpose. In some individuals mental tensions are rebuilt rapidly. In others the pressure may not become overwhelming for several days, or even a month. This variation is perfectly normal. It merely indicates the way in which each individual uses a natural method of releasing mental tensions—to each according to his need.

The average man requires sexual release from one to three times per week. In the sex act, he retains his sensual desires and participates until he has an orgasm. Then he relaxes, the sensuous stimulation evaporates, and he is unable to continue intercourse. If his genitals are persistently stimulated physically, he may have another erection and be able to repeat the sex act. However, sooner or later he reaches a point of maximum depletion of his semen and mental tensions so that further erection and ejaculation are impossible. He must wait until his mental needs build up again. When they do he can engage in the sex act though the products of ejaculation are deficient.

The mental origin of the sex act is essential. If it were merely a physical reflex and nothing more, as the sexperts say, those unfortunate people whose sex organs are destroyed in an accident or are removed because of cancer or other disease would also lose the sex urge. This does not happen. On the contrary, the sex drive often increases when the sex organs are absent. I have had male patients whose penis and testes were crushed in accidents, female patients whose ovaries and breasts, or whose vaginal structures and uterus, were surgically removed. In all, the lust feelings persisted because they are mentally derived.

Frequently a male patient, whose penis had to be amputated because of cancer, undergoes subsequent plastic surgery for reconstruction of the organ out of other body tissues so that he can continue to have sexual intercourse. It is known that castration of eunuchs by removal of their testes did not destroy their sexual needs. Instead the surgical procedure also removed inhibitions, making it possible for them to have lustful affairs with the women of the harem without being detected by the sheik.

The size of the penis is no measure of the male's sexual capacity. In fact, men with abnormally large penile organs may be less capable of having an erection and of leading an active sex life than those with normal or even small organs. The general sense of inferiority connected with a small penis may be related to the infantile castration complex, which was discussed in the preceding chapter. Fear of incapacity, of course, can produce psychological impotence. But as far as physical capacity is concerned, I have never known a patient who could not have satisfactory normal sex relations provided he could develop an erection, regardless of the size of his penis.

The question of circumcision often arises. As far as performance of the sex act is concerned, there is no advantage one way or the other. Circumcision is a matter of male hygiene and preventive medicine. The religious rites associated with circumcision—especially among the Jews, Egyptians, and other Mediterranean peoples—stem from ancient times when all learning was connected with religion. It is amazing that these early teachers should have had such practical knowledge of the rules of human health, which have been substantiated by modern medical science.

Circumcision is a very simple operation, which is most easily performed in infancy. The male is born with a skin sheath over the end of his penis, called the foreskin. Like the appendix, the foreskin is an anatomical remnant from a previous stage of evolution when it served a purpose. Today it is useless and may cause physical problems. At times it becomes swollen and tightens like a noose around the penis, a condition which must be treated immediately before it becomes serious. Irritating secretions tend to collect beneath the foreskin, requiring constant cleansing to prevent sores and tissue damage. Surgical removal of the foreskin allows the penis to remain free of secretions, makes it easier to clean, and prevents serious complications. Cancer of the penis, for example, has been reported only in uncircumcized males— never in those who have been circumcized. The irritations associated with the foreskin may be the cause. If circumcision is performed on a boy past infancy, special care should be taken to explain to him in detail the purpose and procedure of the operation, in order to prevent any emotional disturbance arising from his subconscious fears of castration.

The female is also born with a fold of skin over the clitoris. In many women the clitoris is the primary erotic zone. Very occasionally the prepuce of skin over this organ is completely encompassing and makes it difficult for the woman to attain maximum excitation during intercourse. Some patients are improved by a surgical removal of the foreskin similar to the male circumcision. The procedure is extremely simple, heals rapidly, and may make the marital act more gratifying. If the physician has reason to believe that such treatment will benefit the patient's sexual nature, there is no reason to avoid recommending it.

In Miss Z's case, however, circumcision was not necessary although she thought it was. Miss Z is a nymphomaniac, who seemed to realize she was not enjoying intercourse though she indulged in incessant acts with men. She asked me to circumcize her, for she believed the covering over the clitoris reduced pleasurable sensations and that if the foreskin were removed she would enjoy intercourse more and require it less. Nymphomania is not due to such a cause, and although she insisted on having the operation, I did not agree to do the surgery. She went elsewhere, but afterward decided to return as a patient. She said the results of the operation were most satisfactory, but it was my impression from talk-ing with her on subsequent office visits that she was con-tinuing to indulge in the sex act as a reflex and did not experience any greater pleasure.

Actual castration—surgical removal of the testes—is some-times necessary for reasons of infection or cancer or in-juries. As noted above in connection with eunuchs, this operation does not affect physical potency. Although he can never again fertilize a female ovum, the castrated male is perfectly capable of giving and receiving pleasure in sexual intercourse. The only factors to guard against are psychologi-cal—fear of impotence or embarrassment.

The same factors—fear and embarrassment—are the chief concern in male hernia. A hernia is simply a weakness in the belly wall, forming an opening through which parts of the abdominal organs may find their way. It does not affect or reflect on the male's manhood or sexual potency. A large hernia may interfere anatomically with performance of the sex act, however, or may be esthetically displeasing to the female partner. If the hernia opens into the scrotal sac (the pouch holding the testes), the pressure may interfere with the blood supply and thus damage the testes. Most hernias should be corrected by surgery.

Older men are not infrequently troubled with enlargement of the prostate gland. As previously noted, this gland manufactures secretions which carry the sperm through the male urethra. If the prostate becomes so enlarged that its pressure against the bladder blocks the passage of urine, it must be either partially or totally removed by surgery. Partial removal does not usually affect sexual potency, but if the gland must be entirely removed, sexual potency may be affected. As compensation, however, the man has generally reached the time of life when affection and companionship are more important to him than the sex act and an increase in this aspect of his sexuality can compensate for the physical component.

I have noticed that older couples who remain happily married have kept the spark of romance alive because their marriage is based on the essential ingredient. They may or may not continue to express their love in the physical sex act. It does not seem to matter. They have discovered that sexual needs can be greatly satisfied with a highly developed love component whether or not it culminates in sexual intercourse. Theirs is a perpetual courtship—from the age of youthful anticipation to that of rewarding memories.

XVI

~~~~~~~~~~~~~~~~~~~~~~~~~~~~~~

One Man—One Woman

Simple cells reproduce by bumping into each other and fusing at random. From this basic method the process of mating becomes more and more complex, the higher the development of the species.

Organized animals are extremely selective in choosing a mate. Some birds and mammals are monogamous. The human race has this characteristic also. In addition, the monogamy instinct, which developed to meet the demands for survival of a particular species, is augmented in the human by social, economic, and moral factors.

Children are completely dependent on the monogamous state. Though amoebas can reproduce by simple fusion and though the cow and calf may remain independent of the sire, the child cannot exist securely unless he knows—as expressed in the song, "Summertime"—that mommy and daddy are standing by. From birth and for many years following, the human being is the most dependent of all creatures. Both a mother and a father are needed.

Normal men and women—especially women—are overwhelmingly monogamous. The more important sexual love becomes for an individual, the more it requires being in love with one other person. The greater their love, the more they suffice for each other. It is only when affectionate love is lacking that sex partners will share sensual love with others. An absence of deep personal love between two people weakens jealousy, so that fear of losing the other's affection is then unable to summon up violence to protect the sexual object. In such cases, the sex act temporarily extinguishes erotic desires, and a regression takes place to where love means indifferent sexual relations.

Until the present stage of evolution, in which we are currently participating, the males remained dominant over the females because of superior physical strength. It is only within the past few thousand years, especially under the influence of the Judeo-Christian tenet of individual worth, that women have become more personally aggressive in asserting their instincts of mastery and self-determination. These influences and social conditions have caused some women to rebel from monogamy. Nevertheless, the feminine woman is fundamentally monogamous. Even when she does not confine sexual relations to one man and has frequent affairs, she is usually absolutely monogamous during each relationship.

Failure to satisfy the one woman—one man need can lead to considerable psychological disturbance. Some "liberal-minded" women rationalize that woman's equality requires sexual freedom. The emotional incapacity of these women precludes their having a monogamous relationship. Many suffer from depression; some are masochistic. Many come from broken homes without fathers, some have been prematurely seduced in childhood, and others have experienced mental traumas making it difficult to subjugate their intellects into normal feminine channels. The roots of their rationalizations frequently arise from a reactionary repetition of their earlier life history. There are instincts that have outgrown their original importance, but the monogamy instinct is not one of them.

Monogamous societies have contributed more to humanity than those nations where men maintain women in harems like sheep in flocks.

Some birth-control zealots are campaigning to eliminate monogamy, parenthood, family, and child-parent relationships. The population-control experts proclaim that modern and future societies can best be served if children are placed in communalized home at birth. University specialists would then replace parents and thereby eliminate motherhood and ancestry. The parent substitutes would be trained to instill in the child an allegiance to mankind in general and in this way create citizens for a "Brave New World."

It is regrettable that the Western world, not fully recovered from the ravages of Nietzsche-Hitler philosophies, is becoming gradually enticed by the bizarre intellectualism of these sociological wizards.

Some years ago when I was in training at Bellevue Hospital in New York, the psychiatric wards were filled with sexually distorted patients expounding schizophrenic philosophies. Durng the psychedelic age, the same types of people are out loose, teaching the public how to live.

XVII

Birth Control

A pretty young airline stewardess, volunteering for work in the local hospital during her three-week vacation, came to my office for the required physical examination. I was much impressed with her friendly courtesy and her interesting and intelligent discussion of her work, including the education, training, and special talents necessary to qualify as a stewardess. She was twenty-one and seemed an ideal type of young woman. As we chatted in my consulting room after the examination, she told me she did not plan to marry for another two years, because she wanted to lead her own life "and learn how to assume responsibility."

As the father of five, including three teen-agers, I asked this poised, young adult what she felt parents could do to help their children make a proper adjustment to living in today's world.

"If parents wish their children to behave properly, the best thing to do is to provide a neighborhood where their friends and associates have the same standards and ideals that you want your children to have," she answered simply and rationally. "It's the only way you can be sure that your children will grow up with the proper moral values. They'll do what their friends are doing, irrespective of the parents' advice."

"Thank you," I said. "That's a very sound and logical suggestion."

She smiled pleasantly and rose to leave. Just as she reached the door, she turned suddenly and hurried back to my desk.

"Oh, Doctor, I almost forgot," she said, taking from her purse a small, almost empty vial. "Would you be good enough to write me a prescription for some more of these birth control pills? I got these in St. Louis, and I'll be needing more before I go back."

I am aware that many of my medical colleagues, in all good conscience, provide contraceptives to *all* who ask for them, in the belief that it is better to prevent illegitimate births among people who refuse to abide by the moral standards of our society. However, since I do not consider promiscuous sexual relations to be natural in the present stage of human evolution, I do not write promiscuous anti-pregnancy prescriptions. Under proper circumstances, it is a different matter.

Man has evolved into a monogamous creature, and moral standards have evolved along with him to insure the highest possible fulfillment in marriage for the human male and female. To continue the progress of evolution, it is important that every new human being be given the opportunity to develop his or her full potential. This is not possible in overcrowded conditions.

Therefore I am a strong advocate of birth control for the purpose of limiting the size of families of married couples to the number of children who can be supported, cherished, and reared in adequate circumstances. I have seen too many mothers worn out by a succession of pregnancies, and too many fathers harassed by the pressures of providing for too large a family.

In many countries of the world today, the population explosion is so great and the means are so meager for meeting material needs that human beings are reduced to a status even lower than that of animals. A group of scientists recently conducted a laboratory research experiment concerning overpopulation. They placed a small community of healthy mice in a roomy cage under the best environmental conditions with ample provisions of food and water. For some time the mice lived happily and propagated naturally and profusely. Eventually the cage became literally packed with mice. In this densely overcrowded condition, in spite of the ample supply of provisions, the mice began to ignore normal food and became cannibals—eating one another. Some even attacked themselves. Instead of mating with the opposite sex, they turned into homosexuals. Some of the mice clung to a spot on the wire mesh and went into a trance or coma, wasting away to death.

If even mice become demented and self-destructive when their population becomes too dense, what can be expected of humans? The need for *lebensraum* (living space) has precipitated two world wars within the past fifty years. Statistical reports covering the ratio of exploding population to dwindling supplies and living area indicate that worldwide education in birth control is imperative if mankind is to survive on this planet.

Some religious and philosophical arguments contend that birth control may prevent a great benefactor of humanity from being born. So it may, and that would be unfortunate; but it also without doubt will prevent a horde of suffering human beings from adding their woes to the miseries of humanity.

The purpose of birth control is not to promote sexual promiscuity, but to protect the destiny of every human being who is born into a family, and thus protect the destiny of the human race.

Contraceptive pills, taken by the wife under the direction of a physician, comprise a satisfactory method of controlled prevention of pregnancy.

Normally, once every twenty-eight days, hormone secretions from the pituitary gland activate the female ovaries to release an ovum (egg) into the uterus so that it can be fertilized by the male sperm. Most contraceptive pills or tablets suppress this pituitary action so that no egg is expelled and therefore conception cannot take place. Other preparations prevent a fertilized ovum from attaching itself to the wall of the uterus, making pregnancy impossible. Another type produces a thick barrier of mucus at the cervical entrance which prevents the male sperm from entering the uterus to fertilize the female ovum.

There are several types of medicines, either combinations of female hormones or synthetic hormonal preparations. The physician determines which is best suited to the particular patient, to avoid undesirable side effects. Preexisting conditions in the patient or her history—such as tumors or cancer of the breast or female organs, disorders of the liver or blood vessels, pregnancy, and so on—have to be taken into careful consideration. It is therefore imperative that a woman take these pills only on prescription.

These contraceptive preparations have been used for many years in a great number of cases, and are generally safe under medical supervision. My own patients have not experienced any complications, and the side effects are few and easily controlled. Menstrual periods are usually quite normal and well regulated. Occasionally nausea and spotting between the periods occur, but these problems are readily remedied by adjusting the dosage or changing the medical preparation.

More serious complications are remote, although some have been reported—such as blood clots, inflammation of the blood vessels, loss of hair or excessive growth of hair, gain in weight, thyroid enlargement, and aggravation of conditions such as epilepsy, migraine, or asthma. Whether any or all of these side effects are due to the effect of the medicine or the psychology of the patient, or both, is difficult to determine.

In addition to their use as contraceptives, these medicines

are also used in treating menstrual pain and irregularities, preventing miscarriage, and other female disorders.

New research on contraception has developed a contraceptive device that may turn out to be an improvement over oral contraceptives. The intrauterine device, generally referred to as the IUD, compares favorably in effectiveness to the "pill." Many women are switching from the oral contraceptive to the IUD.

These devices are made with chemically inert plastic of varying shapes, depending on the manufacturer. Properly inserted into the uterine cavity, the IUD simply remains there, "minding its own business," whereas the pill has effects on the entire body.

The IUD is inserted once under sterile conditions by a physician. Few serious side effects have been reported, and reexaminations are infrequent. They may even be used in women who have had no pregnancies. Recently the Soviet Union, after extensive comparative testing with the pill, selected the IUD as the contraceptive method of choice.

Exactly how the IUD prevents pregnancy is not certain; however, the procedure has been used since biblical times. Now, sterile conditions and inert substances have made the method safe.

The rhythm method of birth control is popular, especially with couples whose religious faith forbids or does not condone the use of contraceptives. This method is simply the avoidance of sexual intercourse during the interval when the woman desires it most—from the time the female ovum is expelled from the ovary and while it remains fertile in the uterus. This interval usually begins on the fourteenth day of the menstrual cycle and lasts for several days thereafter. In some women, however, the ovum is expelled on the first day of the menstrual cycle, in others on the last day. In fact, any day of the cycle may be the one. Simple tests by the physician can usually determine the exact days to abstain from intercourse.

Withdrawal is the simplest contraceptive technique, but also the least desirable for sexual satisfaction. The male withdraws his penis from the female vagina just before he has an orgasm, ejaculating his sperm outside. If his timing is not exact, some sperm may be deposited in the vagina before withdrawal and pregnancy may result. This interruption of the sex act at its climax prevents complete release of physical and psychological tensions in both partners, and the continuous practice of the withdrawal technique may produce severe anxiety states.

Sperm barriers, worn by either the male or the female partner to prevent the sperm from entering the uterus, are commonly used contraceptive devices. These are about 70 to 80 percent effective. The main disadvantage is the interruption of the natural flow of presexual love, in order to apply the contraceptive device before participating in the sex act. Since the decision to have sexual intercourse is not generally reached by formal agreement but usually occurs spontaneously, a contraceptive interruption breaks the natural progression of sensuous stimulation.

The male contraceptive is a thin, membrane-like covering for the penis. Fitted over the penis, it catches and holds the sperm at the time of orgasm. If the condom is improperly fitted, however, sperm may escape or the condom itself may slip off inside the vagina during intercourse. Sometimes the material tears before or during the sex act. Maximum pleasure is not achieved, because even this thin membrane serves as a barrier to the full sensation of touch, and it may irritate the female vagina and cause inflammation.

The female diaphragm is a similar contraceptive device used by the female partner. It consists of a thin rubber cup which comes in various sizes. The diaphragm is inserted deep into the vagina at the cervix. The back edge of the cup is fitted behind the cervix and the front edge under the pelvic bone, thus holding the cup firmly in place as a barrier to prevent the sperm from entering the uterus. A physician's services are necessary for the proper fitting of the diaphragm and instructions as to its use.

When used correctly, the diaphragm is an excellent contraceptive. It permits full touch sensation in the contact of penis and vagina and natural completion of the orgasm. The cost of the diaphragm is moderate, and it is easily kept clean for reuse over a long period of time. The physician's instructions must be carefully followed, however, and the diaphragm has to be properly placed for it to be effective as a sperm barrier. Some women also use antisperm jellies or creams in the cup of the diaphragm as an added protection, but these are not necessary if the device is used correctly.

Antisperm chemicals in the form of jellies, creams, or vaginal suppositories are inserted in the vagina as a contraceptive before sexual intercourse, and must be reapplied if the sex act is repeated. These are messy, sometimes irritating, and not too effective. Their use has the same disadvantage, as noted above, of interrupting the natural flow of preliminary lovemaking, plus an unpleasant and unesthetic effect.

Douching is the least effective, the most harmful, and the most extensively used of any contraceptive method. Contrary to all the elaborate ads and garrulous advice, douching as a means of "feminine hygiene" is unnecessary, unnatural, irritating, and damaging—no matter whether plain water or an expensive solution is used.

The vagina naturally has a small amount of secretion which keeps it moist and lubricated. Douching removes this natural secretion, leaving the vaginal walls dry. In an attempt to correct this abnormal dryness, the glands secrete an extra amount of fluid. Since the natural protective bacteria have also been removed by douching, the excess secretions become a breeding place for infectious bacteria. The infection increases the discharge, which may develop an odor or become irritating or both. Instead of leaving nature alone to reinstate the protective bacteria and heal the infection, many a mis-guided female thinks she "isn't clean enough" and takes another douche. This vicious cycle does not merely repeat itself, but gets worse each time. By the time the woman finally comes to her doctor, she may be so sore inside that she can scarcely walk.

Many vaginal discharges are the direct result of excessive douching and can be cleared up completely by simply having the patient stop douching. In some cases medicines may be prescribed to hasten the recovery. From my clinical observa-tion, I suspect that a major cause of cancer in the female organs, which is becoming more and more prevalent, is due to the irritation of these tissues by constant douching.

Even after sexual intercourse, douching is unnecessary to remove the male sperm and semen. Nature has already pro-vided for this procedure. The vagina cleans itself. The mu-cous lining of the vaginal wall normally has a slight forward movement which, after the orgasm, serves to sweep out the excess male secretions. All that the female partner has to do is wipe off the semen when it emerges externally. This natural process may take a little longer than a douche, but it is much healthier.

Sterilization, or "tying the tubes" in the male or female reproductive organs to prevent the germ cells from being expelled is, of course, the surest method of birth control. It gives permanent assurance that the male sperm will not fertilize the female ovum. Sexuality is not affected. In fact, the sex drive may become more intense, because there is no longer any anxiety about causing pregnancy. After a married couple has had the desired number of children, sterilization of either husband or wife can give them much greater freedom in their sexual relations.

Male sterilization is a very simple operation, which can be done by a competent physician in his office. The male tubes are the ducts through which the sperm travel from the testes to the prostate, to be ejaculated with the semen through the penis. This is the only function of these tubes. They have no effect, one way or the other, on "maleness" or "manhood." Tying the tubes merely prevents the sperm from being ejaculated with the semen during an orgasm. The orgasm is just as pleasurable—in fact, even more so, since there is no danger of causing an unwanted pregnancy.

A small incision in the scrotum is all that is necessary for the physician to snip the tubes and close the ends securely by tying them with surgical thread. Normally the incision heals quickly without a noticeable scar. Sexual intercourse may be resumed within a few days. However, contraceptives should be used for several weeks after tying the tubes to be sure the sperm which are already in the prostate gland have been expelled.

Although sterilization for the male is a much simpler procedure than for the female, many men are reluctant to have it done because of misinformation, superstition, or subconscious fear of castration. These psychological barriers need to be removed before the operation is performed.

Possibly because of these same misconceptions, male sterilization is prohibited by law in some states. Others permit it only under certain conditions. Both physician and patient must be sure of the legal regulations.

Female sterilization is often legalized in states which prohibit it in the male. This may be due indirectly to the more uninhibited attitude of women in general toward this surgical procedure. Although the operation is more complicated in the female, many more women eagerly volunteer for it. The female tubes, like those in the male, serve only one purpose. These uterine tubes act as a passageway for the ovum from an ovary into the uterus. A lower abdominal incision is necesary to reach the female tubes, which are deeper in the body. The tubes are then cut and tied, as in the male. Normal recovery is about the same as in an uncomplicated appendix operation. It takes longer to recover than in the male, and the woman will have a scar on her lower belly. However, this will in no way interfere with her sexual pleasures, which usually increase with the removal of anxiety about getting pregnant.

Abortion is the last resort in preventing a birth. It is illegal in most countries, including most of the United States, except when absolutely necessary to save the mother's life. Because of the increasing number of extramarital pregnancies, however, there is a great deal of discussion at present about liberalizing abortion laws to allow medical interruption of pregnancy. In spite of its illegality, however, many thousands of women and girls undergo criminal abortions every year. These are truly criminal when performed—as most are—by quacks and unscrupulous persons using crude methods under unsanitary conditions. If the unfortunate woman or girl survives these circumstances, she may succumb to later infection, or if she recovers she may be sterile for life. In addition to the physical scars, there can be lifelong psychological and emotional scars. Not all illegal abortions have such disastrous consequences, of course, but the danger is ever present.

Because of this situation and the alarming increase in unmarried pregnancies, especially among teen-agers, some states have adopted new liberal abortion laws. It is argued that these laws encourage cases of unwanted pregnancies to consult a physician instead of an illegal abortionist. American Medical Association delegates have reached the decision that they consider abortion a matter between the physician and the patient. Some hospitals and physicians, located in states where abortions have been legalized, advertise, soliciting for abortions from all over the country. Many physicians advocate legalizing medical interruption of pregnancy in cases of rape, incest, strong possibilities of deformities in the child, and physical or mental danger to the mother. Although I am in accord with abortions for these purposes, my agreement ends here.

With no criticism or judgment of my medical colleagues

who advocate *freely* interrupting unwanted pregnancies, my own personal feeling is that unwanted pergnancies should be prevented, not destroyed.

The unwed mother should be helped in every way possible to maintain physical and mental health throughout pregnancy and to achieve the delivery of a healthy baby. If she does not receive understanding help and sympathy from her family, there are a number of institutions and agencies which have been established to provide privacy, financial assistance, and competent guidance. If the unwed mother cannot keep or refuses to keep her baby, adoption services will assist in placing the child in a suitable home, with loving parents who can provide a normal family life.

Modern contraceptives do make it easier for individuals to indulge in illicit and indiscreet sexual relationships. But physical and mental difficulties still result—and so do unwanted pregnancies. Abortion, however, cannot solve the moral and mental problems related to illegitimate pregnancies —it can only worsen them.

XVIII

~~~~~~

Venereal Disease

"Doctor, I don't know what to do. My wife will take the kids and leave me if she finds out that I have gonorrhea," said Mr. Y desperately. "I swear to you, it was an accident! I was down at the bar with the boys, and all of a sudden we decided to take out the girls that we had been talking to there. I was a little drunk, and had no idea anything like this would happen. I love my wife and kids. What'll I do?"

I explained again that Mrs. Y would have to come in for an examination, because it was quite possible that she had contracted the disease from her husband.

"I'll send her in to see you," Mr. Y agreed. "But can't you tell her something to get me off the hook? Can you say that I got it from a toilet seat? The toilet where I work is awfully dirty, and I could have gotten it there. As a matter of fact, that's probably where I did get it," he insisted.

The gonorrhea germ dies very quickly outside its natural environment in the body tissue. There is as much chance of these germs surviving on a toilet seat as of a man surviving on the moon without his space equipment. Yet, a doctor's instinct is always to help his patients. I certainly did not want to precipitate a divorce.

The next day Mrs. Y came in for her examination.

"Mrs. Y," I explained, "it will be necessary for me to

do a female examination on you to take a vaginal smear. Mr. Y was here yesterday for a checkup, and I discovered that hè had an infection of his urinary tract. It is possible that he could transmit this infection to you. Although this may not be the case, it is necessary to be sure."

Unfortunately, the examination showed that Mr. Y had infected his wife. I had to tell her what the disease was, and set up the schedule of treatment.

"I have gonorrhea?" she exclaimed. "What do you mean? My husband has gonorrhea! How did he get it?"

"He says the toilet seat where he works is dirty, and that he picked up the infection there," I explained.

"From a toilet seat?" she repeated.

I did not answer and she did not question me further. A wife seldom does. She usually accepts the information the doctor gives her regarding such matters and lets it go at that. Her reaction may be due to a subconscious wish not to have her suspicions confirmed as to how her husband really acquired a venereal disease. Sometimes life is simpler and pleasanter without stirring up a hornet's nest.

Although tremendous advances have been made in the control and treatment of gonorrhea and syphilis, these venereal diseases still spread their infection. Gonorrhea is especially prevalent today among young people. Not including the armed services, there are an estimated 100,000 cases per year in young Americans between the ages of twelve and nineteen. Incredible as it may seem, some teen-age boys consider "GC" (short for gonococcus, the germ of gonorrhea) to be a "badge of manhood." Their bravado no doubt stems from the apparent ease with which this disease may be cured with modern medicines.

In my medical school years, the treatment for both gonorrhea and syphilis was painful, lengthy, and uncertain. It reinforced the moral prohibitions against promiscuous sexual intercourse.

Since the discovery of penicillin and other medicines,

however, the treatment for venereal disease has become
relatively short and simple, and is usually effective when
the disease is diagnosed in time. If the patient is allergic
to penicillin, other antibiotics may be used. These alternate
medicines are also being prescribed now to treat penicillin-
resistant strains of veneral disease germs which have recently
developed. Germs, too, fight for survival.

Early detection of the disease is important, before either
the gonococcus of gonorrhea or the spirochete of syphilis
enters the bloodstream and infects other parts of the body,
where it may be difficult or impossible to reach with sufficient concentration of antibiotics to destroy the germs.

Since the time when I was in medical school and the
army, syphilis has become a less feared disease. This disease,
in whatever stage of development, may be easily detected
today in a matter of minutes by a simple blood test. Such
a test has become routine for all pregnant women on the
first visit to a doctor or a hospital, because the mother can
transmit syphilis to the unborn child. If the test is positive,
she is treated immediately, and the disease is prevented
from developing in her baby.

The onset of gonorrhea is not difficult to detect in the
male. There is a yellow discharge from the penis and a
burning sensation when urinating. Immediate treatment is
imperative. The first symptoms do not last long and apparently clear up, giving a false sense of confidence. However, the germs may retreat into the prostate gland and
other organs where it is extremely difficult for the medicines to reach and destroy the gonococcus. A lifetime of
misery can result. The prostate becomes swollen and painful, and the man may become sterile. If the gonococcus
also enters the bloodstream, as sometimes happens, it can destroy tissues in other parts of the body, such as the bone
joints and heart. These crippling scars are certainly an excessive price for a youth to pay for a false idea of "becoming
a man."

In the female, the early symptoms of gonorrhea are not as obvious, because the discharge is concealed in the vagina. The germs travel up the uterine tubes, which connect the ovaries with the uterus. Pus pockets form in these tubes, often producing symptoms similar to appendicitis. Frequently scar tissue forms, blocking the monthly passage of the ovum into the uterus, thus causing sterility.

If a woman with gonorrhea does become pregnant, this disease is not directly transmitted to her baby, but the child may become infected at birth during its passage through the mother's vagina. The gonococcus attacks the baby's eyes, and blindness may result. For this reason, it is the rule in hospitals to give every newborn baby preventive eye treatment against gonococcus infection.

Although the germs of gonorrhea and syphilis develop resistance even to new medicines, the human being does not develop a complete immunity to these diseases. Reinfections are not uncommon. Venereal disease may be acquired and reacquired in almost any part of the world, where it has been carried chiefly by the promiscuous sexual activities of tourists, sailors, and soldiers throughout the centuries.

Today, the armed services of many nations try to control the spread of VD by strict regulations. During the occupation of Japan after World War II, for example, part of my duties as regimental surgeon of the Seventh Cavalry Regiment in Tokyo was supervision of VD prevention and control. Every man was required to report for a VD check upon his return from leave. Gonorrhea was the usual "morning after" infection.

The American soldier in Japan followed the pattern of occupation armies throughout history, and he released his pent-up sex urges in a veritable explosion of seduction and rape. Although the geisha houses were declared "off-limits" for enlisted men, the soldiers found accommodation elsewhere. The Japanese women—traditionally chaste, genteel, and subservient to their men—were no match for the aggressiveness of the American GI, who mistook a polite "No thank you" for a coy "Come on." There were also "amateur geishas" who were willing to provide sexual satisfaction in return for extra rations, chocolate, cigarettes, soap, and other material advantages.

As required by the American Army, Japanese authorities attempted to control venereal disease in the native population and thereby help control it in the servicemen. The Japanese police periodically rounded up women from the streets of downtown Tokyo, herded them into trucks and vans, and carted them off to a government facility for VD examination. I was among the U.S. Army doctors asked to assist. It was a humiliating experience, not only for the Japanese women, but for me as an American. Relatively few VD cases were discovered, and these were retained for treatment. Most of the women were virtuous mothers, wives, and daughters of respectable Japanese households who had been attending to their regular duties of marketing and shopping for family needs. After being subjected to the examination, to which they submitted in stoic acceptance of governmental authority, they were allowed to gather up their bundles and walk out the front door. There they were subjected to further indignities by loitering young American soldiers, who not only accosted but literally ran after these women and all but forcibly raped them.

The young men who were guilty of this disgusting conduct were not ordinary "psychopathic hoodlums." Most of them came from average American homes, where they had been taught decent behavior; but, like the Japanese banzai charge, now that restraints were lifted due to wartime conditions, their sexual lusts exploded. Their ancient instincts were stirred by the role in which they found themselves cast —victors in the war between brothers for possession of the tribal harem. The same thing happened with other troops— not only Americans—in other parts of the world.

Left behind were a large generation of war babies having

no father to care for them and unwanted by the Japanese people. Boatloads of these children, now grown, have been sent to other countries. Many have made an exodus to South America where they are accepted without prejudice.

The soldiers returned home after the occupation to father the current generation of legitimate children. Although they resumed many of the former conventional standards of their society, their attitude toward sex did not become altogether civilized. Similar moral laxity was prevalent in civilians on the home front during the war. Returning servicemen and civilians alike, conditioned by the requirements of war and straining to unshackle themselves from wartime restrictions of governmental authority, broke down more of the moral character of civilization. The promiscuous sexual relations and indifference to the true nature of sexuality was proclaimed as "sexual emancipation," and has led to the sexual distortions in the sixties. The pendulum swinging against authority has swung to the extreme. Lawlessness and perversion are at an all time high level. The pendulum will return, but the force of the swing away from the present zenith may cause it to overswing in the opposite direction before it returns to rest.

XIX

～～～～～～～～～～～～～～～～～～～～～～～

Mysteries of Womanliness

According to Hindu legend, when Twashtri—in compliance with Man's request—created Woman and gave her to Man, Man was at first delighted with her charms. It was not long, however, until he found her willfulness and temperamental moods so exasperating that he returned the new creature to Twashtri, stating that he was better off alone. But Man found that once having known Woman, his loneliness was more profound. He remembered her excellent qualities and her exquisite ways. Tormented with longing he went back to Twashtri and begged to have his companion restored to him.

Provoked, Twashtri declared, "You are more changeable than Woman! Make up your mind. If you take her back this time, you must keep her."

"I have no choice," cried Man in despair. "I cannot live with her—but I cannot live without her!"

Women have always been a mystery to men and have qualities innate to themselves. Since so many women have come to me with problems peculiar to their sex, mentally and physically, and since my medical knowledge and clinical experience have proved helpful in finding solutions, I am encouraged to believe that my clinical conclusions may be beneficial to others.

Let me repeat that every case is individual and that generalizations can serve only as guidelines—not as specific treatments. The discussions in this chapter pertain to matters which, during my twenty-two years as a physician, I have found to be helpful to the average woman in understanding nature's purpose in relation to her sexual anatomy and its functions.

Virginity

The loss of virginity is one of the most significant emotional experiences in the life of the average woman. Whether pleasant or otherwise, her first experience in sexual intercourse is unforgettable. Both nature and custom conspire to make it so. In spite of retrogressive celebrations of "free-love" cults such as exist today, the instinctive female reluctance to mating has been upheld throughout the centuries in enduring social practices and evolving moral codes. From childhood, the human female is conditioned to repress her sensual feeling in regard to her genitals. Unlike the male, her sex organs are not easily accessible. Her uterus and ovaries are deep within her body, and even the opening of her vagina is partially closed by a membrane, the hymen. Sexually she remains an anatomical mystery even to herself. In early childhood, the female child has feelings of inferiority about her genital organs. The parents, by teaching and example, change this feeling. Under their influence she learns to have a high regard for femininity and to prize her bodily structures.

In situations where the family or environment debases sex by condoning promiscuity, the female regains her subconscious impression that the female reproductive system is an unclean cloaca.

As she matures physically—and usually by the time she reaches puberty or adolescence, after her menstrual periods

begin—the young woman's vaginal structures become large
enough for her to engage in intercourse. However, in the first
sex act the hymen and other structures are stretched. Instead
of experiencing pleasure as does her male partner, she may
feel an unpleasant sensation. This condition is aggravated if
she is not affectionately and sensually attracted to the male.
Aversion or fear can produce a spasm of the muscles around
the vaginal opening, intensifying disagreeable feelings. Such
a spasm may occur even in mature women, especially if their
sexual attitudes are adverse to the sex act.

It is not the physical unpleasantness of the first sex act
but its psychological effect that can be permanently damaging to the girl or woman. The virginal female indulges in
blissful fantasies of sexual love without understanding just
what it means. The reality of the sex act may fail to
correspond with her dreams. Disillusionment, hurt pride, and
fear of physical discomfort may turn her against any desire
to adjust to a natural sex relationship, and she may well
become frigid. She may develop, too, a resentment of the
opposite sex for aggressiveness and gratifications at her
expense.

There are some fortunate women who enjoy sexual intercourse from their first experience; regardless, however, as
to whether the first sex experience is pleasant or unpleasant,
the human female is enthralled with the first male who
"deflowers" and possesses her. This is one reason for retaining virginity until marriage. If the woman marries for love
—as most women do—her affection for her bridegroom will
minimize any discomfort and emotional fears about her introduction to sexual intercourse. If her husband is the first man
to enthrall her, their chances of happiness together are
greater because she is more likely to find in him her one
true love, and he feels the blissful assurance that she belongs
only to him. When a woman loses her virginity to a man
whom she does not marry, whether she loves him or hates

him his image will inevitably reappear in her memory and intrude at times between her and her husband. Such recollections often cause a wife to feel a sense of betrayal toward her husband, arousing guilt feelings which make her question her loyalty and affection for her husband. She fears her marital experiences are less significant than the first extramarital one.

These subconscious reactions to the loss of virginity do not arise from superimposed inhibitions, but from natural instincts supported by morality. Nature intended virginity to be considered a virtue.

It is true that in primitive societies and among the "free lovers" of today virginity is not a virtue. Some savage people consider it taboo for a husband to be the first man having sexual intercourse with his wife; and if a woman comes to marriage as a virgin, another man in the tribe, usually the priest, is assigned to perform the sex act with her. Lower cultural civilizations consider women mysterious creatures with strange powers over men, and they fear a husband having intercourse with a virginal wife will be possessed by her. The dissimilarities between the sexes arouse hostilities in the minds of savage men, and they resent being influenced or controlled by women. Their marital relationship is not as close as that of our society.

Freud hypothesized that the defloration customs among savages served a useful purpose. He reasoned that if the woman became hostile to her sex partner who deflowered her, it was advantageous to the husband for this hatred to be directed toward another. In this matter, my clinical experience fails to correspond with Freud's assumption.

Love grows between a husband and wife from the experiences they share together. The disagreeable ones are as important to cementing their lives together as the more pleasant ones. Overcoming obstacles to happiness together is important to a complete marriage.

Menstruation and Pregnancy

Menstruation, which is a perfectly natural and normal process, has been surrounded since primitive times by so many superstitions and taboos that some of these misconceptions persist even today. In some women, the bleeding is subconsciously associated with the infantile castration complex and a sense of guilt, as though they are being punished for early Electra feelings toward the father. The most prevalent religious interpretation of this guilt feeling is that menstruation is a "curse" in punishment for "original sin."

There are many superstitions concerning the magical or dangerous qualities of menstrual blood. Actually, this is exactly the same kind of blood as that flowing through the rest of the woman's body. It is neither "bad blood" nor "super blood"—it is just plain blood. The menstrual flow itself consists of normal blood mixed with the sloughed lining from the wall of the uterus.

In some primitive tribes, the menstrual period is believed to occur because the girl or woman is having sexual intercourse with the spirit of a dead ancestor, and it is therefore taboo for a living human being to touch her. This may be the origin of the current notion that a woman should not indulge in the sex act while menstruating. As a matter of fact, there is no reason—other than esthetic ones—to abstain from intercourse at this period of the month.

Menstruation is simply part of nature's cycle in connection with reproduction of the species. The uterus is a pear-shaped organ in the lower abdomen or belly, protected by the pelvic bones. The small end of the pear, the cervix, points downward opening into the vagina, the passageway that extends to the exterior of the body between the labia or "lips" of the female genitals. The vagina is the structure into which the male sperm are ejaculated and from which they make their way into the uterus in anticipation of fertilizing an ovum, which will then develop into an embryo to form another human being.

To the sides of the upper end of the pear-shaped uterus are the ovaries, each about half the size of a golf ball. Connected to the uterus in the area of the ovaries are small ducts, the ovarian tubes. The ovaries contain the female germ cells. Usually every twenty-eight days—with normal variations ranging from twenty to thirty-eight days—one of the ovaries expels an egg, sending it through its tube into the hollow uterus. The ovary forms a cyst—a small sac containing fluid around the ovum—when the egg is to be expelled. After the ovum is expelled, the cyst normally "reduces" or disappears. Occasionally a cyst reduces too slowly or not at all.

To be normal, ovaries must expel eggs and form cysts; if they fail to do so, they are not functioning properly. Not infrequently, these normal cysts are felt on gynecological examinations. Mistakenly, some women have surgery to remove these cysts, and sometimes one or both ovaries are sacrificed as well. Studies at a large Midwestern medical university showed that most ovarian cysts and ovaries removed from women are normal ones.

Fourteen days before the ovum is expelled, nature begins preparing the uterus to receive it under the best possible conditions for reproduction. The pituitary gland—which is located at the base of the brain and regulates hormone production, among other functions—stimulates the ovaries to increase greatly their production of estrogen, the "female hormone." This estrogen causes new blood vessels to form in the lining of the uterus. For two weeks the lining continues to thicken with blood, ready to supply nourishment if the reproductive process takes place.

Normally at this point the egg is expelled. It remains alive for several days. If, during this interval, a male sperm enters the uterus via the vagina, connects with the ovum, and fuses

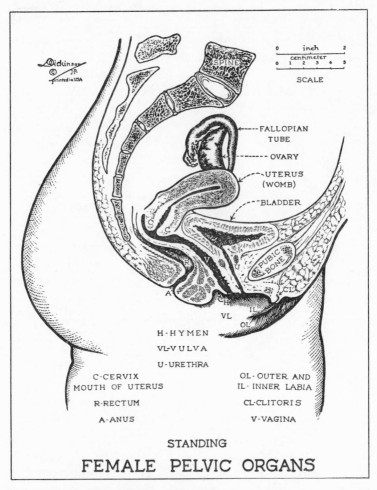

STANDING
FEMALE PELVIC ORGANS

Educational Department, Tampax

with it, the fertilized ovum then attaches itself to the blood rich wall of the uterus and pregnancy begins.

However, if the ovum is not fertilized during this interval, it dries up and is expelled through the vagina during

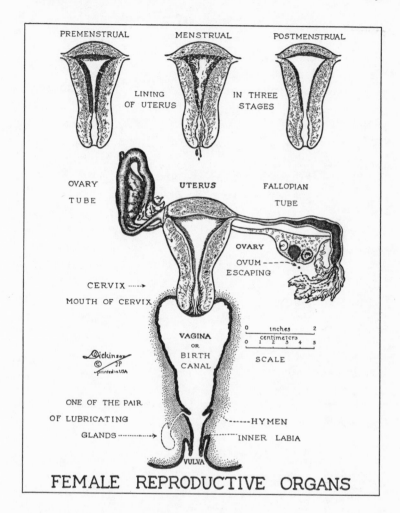

PREMENSTRUAL   MENSTRUAL   POSTMENSTRUAL

LINING OF UTERUS   IN THREE STAGES

OVARY   UTERUS   FALLOPIAN

TUBE   TUBE

OVARY

OVUM ESCAPING

CERVIX ----►

MOUTH OF CERVIX

VAGINA OR BIRTH CANAL

Dickinson © JP printed in USA

SCALE

0   inches   2
0 1 centimeters 4 5

ONE OF THE PAIR OF LUBRICATING GLANDS ---->

------HYMEN

------INNER LABIA

VULVA

FEMALE REPRODUCTIVE ORGANS

menstruation. The ovaries' production of estrogen tapers off, and they switch to producing another female hormone called progesterone. Without estrogen, the new blood vessels of the lining of the uterus cannot survive. The thickened part of the lining sloughs off—very much like peeling off sun-blistered skin too soon—leaving a raw surface beneath. This permits release of the excess blood, which had been stored in the wall of the uterus, allowing the swollen uterus to return to its former state. The flow of the blood carries the sloughed uterine lining with it out through the vagina. The duration of this flow normally lasts from one to ten days, varying with the individual. This normally ends the four-week menstrual cycle and a new one begins.

During the discharge of the menstrual flow, I recommend the use of sanitary napkins rather than tampons. The sanitary napkin, worn outside the genital opening of the vagina, allows the discharge to flow out naturally. The tampon, inserted inside the vagina, absorbs the menstrual flow, retaining it in the vagina. In my opinion, this is an unnatural procedure that can be both chemically and physically irritating to the tissues. I have had patients who were unable to remove the inserted tampon, and some who neglected to do so, remaining unaware of it until they came in for a gynecological examination. Such retention can be damaging.

As the menses passes through the vagina, it accumulates vaginal secretions as well, and the chemical reaction of these substances produces the odor usually associated with menstruation. Effective deodorants to be applied to the sanitary napkin may be purchased at any drugstore. These should be used only externally—never internally.

The average girl begins to menstruate at about age twelve to thirteen, but periods may normally begin anywhere between the ages of ten and seventeen. At either extreme of this age span, however, it is wise to check with a physician to be sure that nothing is functionally abnormal. During the first year or so of menstruation, the periods are usually irregular—sometimes skipping a month or even two, sometimes occurring twice in a single month. If the periods do not fall into a regular cycle by the second year of menstruation, a physician should be consulted. As previously noted, there is a normal variation of the cycle between twenty and thirty-eight days, although twenty-eight days is the average. The amount of flow also varies. Excessively heavy flow may call for medical attention, as too much loss of blood can cause weakness or anemia, or there may be a condition such as an incomplete miscarriage, a tumor, or a hormone imbalance. At the other extreme, when there may be regular but very little flow and the woman cannot become pregnant, it may, but not necessarily, indicate a malfunction of the ovaries which can be medically corrected. Very rarely is any serious surgery (such as surgical removal of the female organs) indicated for menstrual problems.

Emotions and mental attitudes often have a direct effect on menstruation. A healthy woman—physically and mentally adjusted—experiences no actual physical disturbance or discomfort from the natural process of menstruation. Some women, however, have been conditioned by parents, relatives, friends, and others to expect and fear difficulties during the menstrual period, such as "cramps" or similar complaints. Unfortunately, psychosomatic pain hurts the patient just as much as physical pain, and she must be given relief. A change in attitude and an understanding of menstruation are, of course, the best remedies. I often use the analogy of the first stages of labor, when the uterus contracts violently but without any sensation of pain or "cramps" to the mother. Many a pregnant woman has barely made it to the delivery room in time because she waited until she felt pain before calling her doctor. Labor pains do not usually begin until the baby's head starts pushing into the vagina. In menstruation, there is no stretching of the vagina, and any natural contractions of the uterus in expelling the accumulated blood are far less intense than those at the beginning of labor. Only in rare cases do menstrual "cramps" have a real physical origin.

Emotions do affect glandular function, and emotionally upset women are most prone to menstrual difficulties.

Irritability just prior to or during menstruation—known as premenstrual tension—may be emotional, or it may have a physical origin. Frequently it is due to a hormone imbalance. Normally, after producing the additional estrogen necessary to prepare the uterus for receiving the ovum, the ovaries shift smoothly into the production of progesterone if the egg is not fertilized and does not attach itself to the lining of the uterus. In some cases, however, the ovaries get their signals mixed, and they keep on manufacturing excess estrogen, or do not make enough progesterone to help bring about the normal process of menstruation. The usual symptoms are heaviness in the pelvic region and sometimes in the breasts and an apparent gain in weight which is due to water being retained in body tissues. This retention is caused by salt retaining water in the body. The condition can be easily relieved by omitting salt from the diet for about ten days prior to menstruation. To avoid the tastelessness of a completely salt-free diet, the intake of salt may be reduced and the intake of water increased (since drinking excess water acts as a diuretic) along with medically prescribed dosages of ammonium chloride, which helps the kidneys to eliminate excess water from the tissues. Some physicians prescribe diuretics, strong medicines which directly stimulate the kidneys, but I prefer not using these except in cases of waterlogging due to kidney conditions or heart failure. For premenstrual tension, I have found ammonium chloride preferable or—if expense is not a problem to the patient—a prescription of progesterone hormone, which obtains excellent results.

Failure to menstruate, especially in a married woman, immediately suggests pregnancy. This condition can usually be verified within six weeks by a gynecological examination. At this time there is a characteristic "feel" to the pregnant uterus which the experienced physician recognizes. Other signs include breast enlargement, spotting (small discharge of blood as the embryo attaches itself more firmly to the uterus), morning sickness, and so on. Certain laboratory tests may also be used, with varying degrees of accuracy. Sometimes medicine is given which will bring on menstruation if the patient is not pregnant but will help retain the fertilized ovum if she is.

If pregnancy is not the cause of a missed period, it may be due to emotional causes or an estrogen deficiency. Or it may be merely a normal "skip" such as occurs occasionally. Whatever it may be, the cause should be medically determined.

If a young girl fails to start menstruating at the usual age, she may be merely late in developing, or it may be due to several other causes. Normally there is an opening in the center of the hymen, but sometimes this membrane completely closes the entrance to the vagina. A simple operation is necessary to correct this condition. There may be a glandular disturbance or a congenital defect. A physician's advice should be sought.

In any and all problems concerning menstruation, the important point to remember is that the female menstrual cycle is a perfectly natural occurrence. There is nothing mysterious or dangerous about it, nothing to be feared or ashamed of. Whether the process begins early or late, whether the periods occur every twenty, twenty-eight, thirty, or thirty-eight days, whether flow lasts one day or ten, makes no difference. It has no effect on the female sex drive one way or the other. Menstruation is merely nature's way of disposing of nourishment prepared for a pregnancy which did not take place. The tissue of the uterus is the same as that of the rest of the body, the blood the same as if a finger had been pricked. Menstruation may sometimes be an inconvenience or an annoyance, but it is as natural a one as hunger or thirst.

Menopause

Menopause is simply the end of menstruation. It ends
very much as it began. Somewhere between ages forty and
sixty-five—usually in the average woman at about age forty-
five—the menstrual periods start to become irregular. A
month or two may be skipped, there may be a very large flow
one month, very little the next. Again, it is nothing to become alarmed about. Like menstruation, menopause is a
perfectly natural occurrence. Nature is, in effect, saying
that the woman has done her job as far as reproducing
the species is concerned, and now she is entitled to rest and
freedom.

The psychological aspects of menopause were discussed
in Chapter 4. This event does, indeed, usher in "the best
years of life" for a woman. She is now freer than she
ever was—and she has accumulated experience in living
so that she can enjoy these years to the fullest. Menopause
should be welcomed—not dreaded. As with menstruation,
its problems are more mental and emotional than physical.

The basic physical change which occurs is that the ovaries
stop producing the additional amount of estrogen necessary
to prepare the uterus for pregnancy. Until the entire body
adjusts to this glandular change, there may be minor discomforts. The chief complaint in menopausal women is
experiencing hot and sometimes cold flashes. A hot flash is
a momentary sensation of sudden warmth, often accompanied by a flush over the face and skin. A cold flash is the
reverse. The frequency and discomfort of these flashes
vary in different individuals. They are caused by an over-
action of the pituitary gland in its attempt to stimulate
the ovaries to produce more estrogen. As soon as the pituitary
adjusts to the new situation, the flashes cease. In the meantime, the discomfort may be relieved by doses of estrogen,
either by mouth or by injection. Similar doses of estrogen

are used to relieve high blood pressure, headaches, and dryness of the vagina, which also occur more or less frequently during menopause.

If female hormone medicines are used to treat menopausal symptoms, I find they should be given as nature uses them—that is, prescribed to be taken for the first three weeks and then stopped for seven to ten days. After the rest period the hormones can be given again in the same way. Treatment may be necessary for many months. This schedule follows nature's pattern. If a period or periods recur as a result of hormones, it is of no importance providing it is a "normal" menstruation and entirely due to the medication.

Some doctors routinely prescribe estrogen for all menopausal cases. However, my clinical experience, to date, has been to follow the teaching of a gynecology professor, Dr. Emile Novack, at John Hopkins University and the University of Maryland, who advised prescribing estrogen only in cases of the specific complaints noted above.

My experience has also verified Dr. Novack's advice that the cessation of menstrual periods in a woman under forty should never be diagnosed as natural menopause. Except when the female reproductive organs have been removed by surgery, I have never known menopause to occur in a woman younger than forty years of age. Other causes for the failure to menstruate must be sought, as discussed previously in this chapter.

Occasionally a woman will continue to menstruate and have hot flashes into her early sixties. In such case, she should consult her physician, to determine whether this condition is a normal (for her) continuance of the menopause, or if it is due to another cause which requires attention.

As with so many problems concerning women, the problems of menopause arise chiefly from mental and emotional attitudes. The woman who is physically healthy and has a wholesome, realistic outlook on life has little or no difficulty during this brief transitional period from her childbearing days to complete sexual freedom. Menopause, after all, is nature's own permanent contraceptive.

Female Surgery

Hysterectomies (surgical operations for removal of the uterus) and removal of ovaries should be resorted to only when absolutely necessary—in cases of cancer or some other serious disease which cannot be treated by any other means. Much as I respect all physicians, I am uneasily aware of the tendency of the surgeon to regard the patient merely as a diseased or damaged organ, not as a complete human entity. Yet it is vital to consider all aspects—mental and emotional as well as physical—before partially or totally removing a woman's sex organs.

In hysterectomies due to noncancerous causes, for example, it is customary for the surgeon to remove the entire uterus including the cervix, even though a partial amputation would cure the condition for which the surgery is done. It is rationalized that, at some later date, a cancer might possibly develop in the retained part. To me, this makes as much sense as if the stomach were removed because the appendix is diseased on the assumption that an ulcer may develop later on.

In many women, the cervix can be a major erotic zone. To remove this sensitive part of her sex anatomy is to deprive her of sensual pleasure in the sex act. Except where truly necessary, as in cancer, I see no justification for total hysterectomies which make some women sexual cripples. (Aside from the sexual problems, the cervix supports the upper end of the vagina, keeping it from sagging.)

I recall Mrs. G., a stunning woman of twenty-eight, who came to my office shortly after she had moved from another city. She was very despondent because she no longer enjoyed sexual relations with her husband, whom she loved deeply.

Prior to a "female operation" the previous year, Mrs. G and her husband had shared a blissfully happy sex life. Since her operation, however, she said that sexual intercourse left her "cold." She did not know why surgery had been performed.

When I examined her, I discovered that she had a total hysterectomy, with both the uterus and the cervix entirely removed. She had completely healed and was perfectly healthy. Obviously her cervix had been a highly sensitive erotic zone. Now, without it, she could not have an orgasm or experience any sensual pleasure in her marital sex relations. Her only hope of renewing the important sexual component of her happily married life was to try to develop another genital erotic zone, such as the labia or clitoris.

After a hysterectomy some women, especially if they are childless, become depressed because they cannot become pregnant. Others, however, develop much more interest in sexual intercourse. This new zest is due to two paradoxical factors. One is the removal of a previous fear of becoming pregnant, resulting in greater freedom in sexual relations. The other is the subconscious instinctive desire of the female to bear children, which activates the instinct for mastery to overcome her present inability to do so. If such a woman's major erotic zone has been removed, as in the case of Mrs. G, her intensified sex drive brings no sensual satisfaction and produces frustration and mental tensions. However, if the genital erotic zone remains intact, her sex life will be more enjoyable than before.

Removal of both ovaries in a young woman not only makes her barren but also cuts off the normal supply of estrogen and brings on premature menopause. Such artificially induced menopause is far more disturbing physically and emotionally than when it occurs naturally at the proper age. Hot flashes are usually more frequent, the patient generally gains weight, and her mental tensions produce a variety of psychosomatic complaints. She becomes a pathetically miserable woman.

I believe that the ovaries should never be removed except in cases of cancer, or other extreme conditions—and whenever possible at least a portion of one should be left intact because even this small part will make it possible for the woman to continue a normal life after surgery.

Operations for "cystic ovaries" are becoming increasingly popular, although this type of surgery is very rarely necessary. As explained in the discussion on menstruation, an ovary is normally a cystic organ. The ovaries form cysts around the ovum to be expelled. This tiny sac of fluid normally disappears during menstruation. If it remains and/or enlarges, the condition is almost always self-limiting and corrects itself sooner or later.

However, many women undergo surgery for this uncomplicated condition because of emotional disturbances, for which psychiatry would be the correct treatment.

Mrs. N, for example, was a capable young registered nurse at a hospital to whose staff I belonged. At twenty-six, she had been married only a year when her husband was sent overseas on military service. She was very much in love with him and quite lonely during his absence. One evening her loneliness got the better of her judgment, and she went out with one of the interns. The night's pleasure culminated in a hotel room, where Mrs. N awakened the next morning filled with remorse.

Later that day she came to my office complaining of severe pain her lower right side. Upon examination, I felt a small cystic mass about the size of an olive on the right ovary. I explained to Mrs. N that such a cyst was quite normal, and that it was unlikely that it could cause her to feel any pain. It was then that she told me of her recent indiscretion and self-reproach.

I was sure then that her pain was psychosomatic, caused by her sense of guilt and the subconscious need for punishment. However, as I have already mentioned, psychosomatic pain is nevertheless real pain, so I admitted Mrs. N to the hospital for further observation. The hospital superintendent, concerned about the illness of his employee, asked me to call in Dr. Z, the staff gynecologist, and I obliged. Dr. Z decided to perform an emergency operation and asked me to assist. We found the anticipated small cyst from which an ovum had recently been expelled, but which had not yet dried up. Dr. Z pricked the sac deftly with his scalpel, releasing the small amount of fluid, then neatly sewed up the abdominal incision.

Mrs. N felt greatly improved and recovered normally. She was no longer emotionally disturbed by feelings of guilt and remorse. Her subconscious need for punishment had been fulfilled by the operation and the discomfort that follows abdominal surgery, so she no longer had a subconscious urge to punish herself. She had atoned for her sin and was therefore absolved of guilt.

A less ethical or less knowledgeable surgeon than Dr. Z might well have removed Mrs. N's perfectly normal ovary or ovaries. Psychosomatic pelvic pain is frequently the symptom not of organic trouble but of an illicit love affair. Many a normal pair of ovaries goes down the drain as a result—and the unfortunate woman not only pays the price of the operation, but continues to pay in the physical and mental discomforts of the premature menopause. As an alternative, psychiatric help would be less costly and more beneficial.

Surgical removal of the female organs is indicated, in my opinion, only in cases of severe disease or injury—and if cancer is not the problem, only the part actually diseased or damaged should be removed. To do otherwise, it seems to me, is to cripple the woman just as surely as if the entire hand were amputated because of an infected hangnail.

XX

~~~~~~~~~~~~~~~~~~~~~~~~~~~~~~~~~~

Sex Exceptions—The Happy
Careerists and Others

As we have discussed, when a man and a woman "fuse" in the sex act but fail in companionship, the initial loneliness persists. Or when the essential affectionate love is present but there is no gratifying physical fusion, their life is incomplete. They are only sharing half a loaf of love. If a man-woman relationship exists without either of these components, it is empty. In any of these cases, the usual result is mental distress and a tendency, in one way or another, to release sexuality through other channels—eating, dreaming, aggressiveness, etc. How, then, is it possible for some people to make a satisfactory life adjustment and achieve happiness or contentment in spite of the lack of one or both components of human sexuality? It is because these exceptional individuals have been able to sublimate, or redirect, their libidinal instincts in such a way that there are no residues of loneliness. The adjustments of the sex exceptions would seem abnormal for the average person but become normal for these people.

Suppose, for example, in a happy, completely united married couple, one of the partners develops a cancer of the genital organs or has an injury which makes genital sexual relations impossible. Are they to give in to despair and accept a lifetime of longing for a complete togetherness with another human being? There is no need for them to do so. Any part of the human body can be aroused sensually. New erotic zones can be developed, from which sexual pleasure can be derived. The new primary area relies on excitations from oral, anal, visual, or touch sensations for developing orgastic responses. In physically handicapped individuals, this is not perversion.

When the genital sex act can be performed naturally but a substitute stage of earlier sexual development is preferred, its avoidance is a distortion of reality.

In the case of our hypothetical couple, however, a change in reality has taken place which makes performance of the genital sex act impossible. The substitution of another form of sexual satisfaction therefore becomes normal for them under the changed conditions. It is an adaptation for survival. Anal, oral, visual, and other sensual excitations can normally replace the genital sex act in such circumstances.

At times, substitutes for affectionate needs must be found when circumstances preclude such love. A physical cancer or amputation is much easier to detect and understand than a psychological one. Yet the psychological absence of one or both components of human sexuality occurs far more frequently. The compensation for this lack is more difficult to achieve, but some people are able to do it.

Positive Adjustments

Mrs. C is a good example of a positive adjustment which sex exceptions of this type can make. The oldest child of parents who were indifferent to their children's needs, she mothered four younger brothers and sisters. To escape from this tedious existence, she married immediately after graduating from high school. As is so often the case, however, she duplicated the situation from which she was trying to escape. Her husband was a likeable young man, devoted but completely dependent upon her. Quiet and unassuming, he was not in the least aggressive either as a lover or as a provider. Mrs. C became more bored and discontented than she had been in her previous home life. With her family she had repressed her natural longings for affection and approval, but now these clamored for expression.

Instead of staying at home and becoming a neurotic, Mrs. C got a job as a stenographer. She found real joy in her work and discovered that she was happiest when she was working hardest. Her intelligence and capability soon won her a promotion. Equally rewarding was the affectionate esteem accorded her by the other workers. Her interest in business was stimulated, and she started studying in her spare time at home, although never neglecting her domestic responsibilities. When, in a couple of years, she had a child, Mrs. C resigned from her position to fulfill her duties as a mother.

Within a year, however, her tensions returned at home. Fond though she was of her husband, he contributed so little to her complete sexuality that Mrs. C felt almost as though she were taking care of two children. Although the expense of a housekeeper would take most of her own salary, Mrs. C went back to work. Again her zest for living flourished. The pattern was repeated with her second child, except that by this time Mrs. C's earning capacity had increased so that she could well afford domestic help. She continued with this arrangement until both children were married. Then Mrs. C decided she had fully met the demands of duty and made the final break with family life by divorcing her inadequate husband.

Now in middle age, Mrs. C is a happy and successful businesswoman, completely on her own. Her affectionate love needs are fulfilled within herself and in the friendship and regard of business associates. Her physical sex needs are satisfied in affairs with men friends, whose companionship she also enjoys. She differs from the frantic free lovers, because to Mrs. C the sex act is not an end and aim in itself. It is a pleasant, natural component of the full life she has made for herself. Her career and her interest in her activities supply the essential ingredient. She is her own helpmate.

Some career women and especially some proponents of women's liberation have a deep, instinctive resentment of men. Their vigorous instincts of self-mastery and self-determination spur them to achieve a high proficiency in their chosen fields, rivalling and surpassing their masculine competitors. In their determination to excel men in every way, these women careerists develop their own sex drives to a capacity that equals or exceeds that of the male. To them, a man is merely a necessary sexual expedient. Because all their libidinal energies are self-contained and consumed in their careers, there is little or no affectionate love left over for their sex partners. For satisfactions, these women must have an orgasm with every sex act. If they don't, the man is considered a poor lover. It is this type of woman, who has learned to have consciously induced orgasms more spontaneously than the average woman, who spreads the word that all women should have this kind of sex life.

These women are not promiscuous in the usual sense of the word, and they are certainly not necessarily nymphomaniacs. They are married to their careers or causes. They are not lonely, because they are unified within themselves. Their affectionate love is fused to themselves with appreciation for their accomplishments. Their sensual love is satisfied in sexual relations with men. Should such a woman marry, she and her husband would most likely find great pleasure in the sex act, but it is very doubtful that she could redirect her affectionate love or become a helpmate to him. He would have to accept her as a lordly, energetic lady; it is unlikely she could be a helpmate to anyone but herself.

This same type of adjustment is prevalent among unmarried career men, but it has been generally accepted for so long that it is usually considered standard. As women have become more independent, this type of male is coming into disrepute as a husband. In his defense, let it be said that many a husband becomes married to his work because he does not find a helpmate in his wife.

A number of women make a very happy "normal" adjustment to life without sexual intercourse. I have known an unmarried schoolteacher, for example, who has found a full and rewarding life without a love affair, by sublimating or redirecting all her libidinal energies into teaching and helping youth. Such teachers not only enjoy self-companionship, but their affection overflows to the hundreds of boys and girls who fill their classrooms year after year. The same holds true to an even greater extent for people who are totally dedicated to humanitarian causes, directing their repressed sexuality outward to all mankind. Albert Schweitzer and Mahatma Gandhi are notable examples of this type. In this select category are great religious leaders such as Moses, Buddha, and Jesus. Such genuine humanitarians are the opposite of ascetics—whether religious or beatnik —who release their sexuality in part to improve society in their own way and in part as aggressive energy against themselves.

The normal sex exceptions do not wither away their lives or become embittered, wishing for love denied them by circumstances. They direct their affectionate needs into creative activities—work which is appreciated by themselves and others—and they receive affectionate love from the fruits of their accomplishments. They feel esteem for themselves, which is supported by their achievements, and they occupy a position of importance in the community of man. Their self-esteem is not narcissistic. It is true and justified regard for themselves. Their normal sexuality is completed in genital sex relations with the opposite sex

Negative Adjustments

At the opposite end of the spectrum are those sex exceptions who make a negative adjustment for survival by misdirecting or completely repressing their love energies. They expect neither to love nor to be loved. They may appear to be normal people—but are on the borderline of mental illness.

People are the way they are, to a large extent, because of early childhood experiences; and the following examples of negative sexceptions are given without any intention of condemnation.

The Intellect:

In adolescence, some girls suppress their feminine emotions. Feminism and intuition fail to develop. As women, these girls become all intellect. They may develop into brilliant workers, but work, play, and artistic pursuits are not satisfactory substitutes for feminine needs.

The Progressivist:

Psychoanalysis reveals that the type of zealous woman, championing total sexual emancipation for women and carnal sex education for children, inwardly holds tight to childhood sexual fantasies. She regards the sex act as abusive to women, and she feels that her genital structures are inferior to that of the male's.

The Passive Resister:

Such was the case with Mrs. E, whose mother died in childbirth. She grew up under the repression of an unloving father and a succession of exacting stepmothers who made her feel so unworthy of any consideration that she felt guilty for any happiness in her life. Her only pleasures were found in eating and in withdrawing to her room to loaf and read. When she was called fat and lazy, she passively accepted the criticisms as her due.

Except for being overweight, she was an attractive girl. For a brief interval in her late teens she slimmed down to normal size, won the attention of an overbearing young man very much like her father, and married him. Conditioned as she was to consider herself unworthy of giving or receiving love, Mrs. E was completely passive in affectionate and sexual relations with her husband. She resumed diverting her sexual energies to eating and stuffing herself with fattening foods. When her husband berated her for overeating and for neglecting the housework to sit around and read, she accepted his criticism meekly. During intercourse she merely acted as the receptacle of his sperm. She conceived and bore him a child, who became merely another object of neglect.

This pattern of their lives continues today. They now have three children, whom Mrs. E regards with passive indifference. She is fatter than ever. Dutifully she takes the reducing pills her husband brings home for her—and goes right on eating and gaining. When he angrily throws away the magazines and paperbacks that she dotes on, she says nothing. As soon as he leaves for work, she resupplies herself.

Thus does Mrs. E assert the last vestiges of her survival instincts. She has eroticized eating, and uses it as a substitute for sexual and affectionate pleasures. In this way, as well as in her neglect of home and children, she also feebly manifests her instincts of mastery and self-determination. If she were deprived of these last outlets for libidinal energy, she would very likely collapse mentally and emotionally.

There would be a similar result if her negative adjustment to reality were disturbed by divorce or by a change which would bring her happiness in her life. For Mrs. E, the abnormality of existing as a "vegetable" is normal.

SECTION TWO

Perversity

XXI

~~~~~~

Sterility and Impotence

Sterility and impotence are two entirely different matters. Yet many a couple remains unhappily childless because of the confusion of these two terms, particularly by the husband. He fears that sterility carries with it the stigma of impotence. It does not. A man may be very potent sexually and at the same time be sterile. Potency is the ability to have normal sexual intercourse, regardless of whether or not it results in pregnancy.

Impotence, as will be discussed later in this chapter, means the inability to perform the sex act because of psychological barriers. Mental and emotional disturbances interfere with the natural physical functions of the sex organs.

Sterility

Sterility is a problem which confronts normal couples who can and do enjoy sexual intercourse, but who—for one reason or another—cannot produce offspring. Sterility is concerned with the fusion of the male and female germ cells, nothing else. In the male, it involves the quantity or quality of his sperm, which can be readily determined by a simple test. Because the female sex organs are more complex, the cause of female sterility is not so easily determined. These tests are also simple, but they require more time. Wives, however, are usually very cooperative. Their instinctive desire to bear a child far outweighs any concern about sexual potency.

From nature's standpoint, the best time for a couple to start their family is during their twenties. If contraceptives have not been used and pregnancy has not occurred within three years of the marriage, and the couple wants children, this is the time to seek medical help. The tests and the treatment for sterility may necessarily be prolonged because the wife's menstrual cycle is usually involved. As a rule, the longer the couple delays, the fewer chances there are to correct the cause of sterility and achieve a successful pregnancy.

For this reason, among others, I was far from optimistic when Mr. and Mrs. J, childless after twelve years of marriage, came to seek my help. They longed for a child, but from all appearances they seemed the least likely to succeed. Both were overweight. Mr. J had a high-pitched voice and feminine mannerisms. Mrs. J had masculine build, with broad shoulders and chest and narrow hips, hair on her upper lip, on the sides of her cheeks, and on her chest.

The genitals of both, however, were perfectly normal for the appropriate sex, and they enjoyed natural sexual intercourse. Both were very cooperative on the tests. I found that Mr. J's sperm count was below the quantity necessary to effect a pregnancy. I prescribed thyroid, and within several months his sperm count came up to normal. He was now fertile as well as potent.

I then turned my attention to Mrs. J and discovered that she, too, was sterile. Her menstrual periods were fairly regular, but no ovum was being expelled. For her, I prescribed a hormone combination to stimulate the ovaries to expel the monthly ovum. Before the time elapsed for tests to determine if this treatment was successful, the ultimate test was passed with flying colors. Mrs. J became pregnant.

Nine months later I delivered a beautiful baby girl to

a very happy couple. Fifteen months after that, I officiated at the birth of a handsome boy baby. Twelve months later, another fine boy arrived. And two years after this one, came another lovely girl. It seemed that once Mr. and Mrs. J got started they couldn't stop.

After the birth of their fourth child, this once sterile couple appealed to me for help to curb their fertility. Now in their forties and in a medium income bracket, Mr. and Mrs. J felt that their family was as large as they could take care of adequately. In contrast to their earlier married life, fear of pregnancy was interfering with the pleasure of their sexual relationship. Under these circumstances, I agreed to make Mr. J permanently sterile by tying his tubes. Since then, the couple has continued to live happily.

The reason for testing the husband first in cases of sterility is that, no matter what his wife's condition, she cannot get pregnant if his sperm is deficient. If a physical examination reveals no cause for sterility, the sperm test is made. The man masturbates to produce an orgasm and expel his sperm and semen into a clean receptacle. This specimen must be kept at body temperature and tested immediately. If the man produces the specimen at home, he must bring it at once to the doctor's office, carrying the receptacle under his armpit or somewhere else close to his body to keep the sperm warm. If the sperm count and characteristics are normal, the husband is fertile, and the cause of sterility must be found in his wife.

If the sperm is abnormal in any way, either in quantity or quality, treatment is prescribed. The thyroid gland, located in the neck in front of the trachea (windpipe), is checked, because its secretions affect sperm production. If this is the cause of sterility, it can usually be corrected by thyroid treatment. In other cases various hormones may be effective. Unfortunately there is no guarantee of the success of any medicines known today. If none works, it may be advisable to examine a tiny sample of tissue of the testes. This procedure is called a biopsy, and is quite simple, harmless, and often useful in diagnosis.

If the husband's sperm is normal or becomes normal, and pregnancy still does not result, the wife's sterility tests are begun. If a physical examination shows her sex organs to be normal, the first step is to assure regular menstruation. Strange as it may seem, I have found contraceptive pills one of the best methods of establishing a regular menstrual cycle, which frequently results in fertility. When a woman whose periods have been irregular takes these pills for several months, then stops taking them, her menstruation usually assumes a normal pattern. Sometimes this is all that is necessary to assure fusion of the male and female germ cells.

In some cases, however, menstruation may be or become regular without an ovum's being expelled into the uterus. There are several ways of determining this. The simplest is to collect samples of the cells at the mouth of the uterus at the time of menstruation and by microscopic examination discover whether or not certain hormones are present. A longer but more specific method is to make a graph or chart of daily body temperature over a test period of several months. Since the fluctuations in normal temperature are very slight, a special thermometer is used. The graph will show not only whether an ovum is expelled, but also—if it is expelled—on exactly which day of the menstrual cycle. If no ovum is being given off by the ovaries, the corrective treatment is similar to that of the male—thyroid, hormones, or various combinations of either or both. Here again, there can be no guarantee that these medicines will succeed, although many times they do.

Abnormal vaginal discharges can prevent the male sperm from reaching the uterus. The most frequent cause of such discharges is douching, as discussed in Chapter 15. Usually these discharges will disappear and the vagina be restored to its normal state by stopping the unnatural and unhealthy procedure of douching.

Sometimes the uterine tubes, through which the ovum travels to the uterus, are blocked due to a birth defect, scar tissue from an infection, or some other cause. The fusion of ovum and sperm that results in pregnancy usually occurs while the ovum is in one of these passageways. To determine whether one or both tubes are blocked, a simple and painless procedure is used to inject a special fluid into the uterus, then X rays are taken. The X-ray photographs reveal whether or where the tubes are blocked and also whether or not there is a tumor in the uterus. Sometimes the pressure of the fluid itself will open the tubes. Otherwise, the condition may be corrected by careful surgery. Surgery, of course, is indicated in case of a tumor.

Occasionally there are deformities in the sex organs, such as a double uterus or a double vagina, which must be corrected by surgery. There is no guarantee that such operations will correct sterility—but if the couple really want a child, every possible method must be explored.

The timing of sexual intercourse is important in producing pregnancy. The ovum is most readily fertilized on the day that it is expelled from the ovary and starts on its way down the uterine tube. For five days prior to this day, the couple should abstain from intercourse, because it takes five days for enough sperm to accumulate in the male glands to produce pregnancy. Although the ovum is fertilized by only a single sperm, the mathematical chances of its reaching the ovum have been calculated. It might be compared to the mating flight of the queen bee, who soars high into the air pursued by numbers of male bees—but only one male is strong enough to reach her. So it is with the male sperm and the female ovum.

Suppose that the wife is or becomes fertile, but the husband's sterility cannot be corrected—what then? Artificial insemination may be successful. Children born as the result of this method are loved by both parents and considered as their own. It is important that the donor be entirely unknown to either husband or wife, and that his genetic background assure that he will provide satisfactory sperm. The physician obtains the sperm from the donor in the same manner that the specimen from the husband was obtained. A receptacle containing the sperm is then placed at the mouth of the wife's uterus, to release the sperm under the best possible conditions for fertilization of the ovum.

If artificial insemination does not produce pregnancy or if the couple object to this method for any reason or if the wife's sterility cannot be corrected, I advise the adoption of a child. The ideal method is to make arrangements through an adoption agency to obtain the child of an unwed mother immediately after birth. In my opinion, it is essential that the real mother and the adoptive parents remain forever unknown to one another. Otherwise complications may result for the child. Adoption at birth, of course, cannot always be arranged, but happy results can also be obtained by adopting older children. Adoption agencies are generally quite expert in "matching" the child and the new parents. There is nearly always deep mutual love between adopted children and parents.

It often happens that after an adoption, an apparently sterile couple have natural children of their own. Why this happens is a matter of conjecture. Perhaps the parental feelings aroused by the adopted child in some way stimulate the sex organs or glands into activity. The physical influence of mental suggestion was certainly demonstrated in the case of Sara.

Like Mr. and Mrs. J, Sara and her husband had been married seven years without being able to produce a child, and both proved to be sterile. However, nothing worked in their case. They were fortunate in finding the ideal situation —a baby that they could adopt at birth.

At the time this arrangement was made, the agency informed them that the unwed mother was about four or five months pregnant. Sara, who was a graduate nurse and had cared for a number of pregnant women, began to develop all the symptoms of pregnancy. As the date of the baby's birth drew near, she developed fullness in her pelvis, and came to my office complaining of back pain and difficulty in urinating. Two weeks before the baby was due, Sara duplicated the symptoms of the womb "dropping" into position for delivery. If I had not known the true situation, I would have alerted the hospital for a tentative reservation in the maternity ward.

After the baby was born and adopted, Sara's breasts produced milkish secretions. She and her husband took great joy in their baby, to whom they gave excellent and loving care. Their plans to adopt a second child within a year, however, were changed when Sara herself really became pregnant. She has borne two children of her own and now uses the rhythm method to avoid further pregnancies.

Psychiatric treatment of husband or wife or both has, in several cases that I have known, overcome apparent sterility of many years' duration. Some of these individuals have phobias (abnormal fears) about pregnancy or parenthood which make them sexually impotent. Once these emotional problems are solved with phychiatric help, normal sexual functions are restored. These are cases not of actual sterility, but of impotence.

Impotence

Some physicians attribute frigidity, as female lack of sexual response in the sex act is called, to mental attitudes primarily, but they contend that male impotence may be caused by physical as well as mental factors. I must confess that early in my practice I also held to this theory. More than twenty years of clinical experience, however, have taught me differently. Both male and female impotence have similar mental origins in an unresolved Oedipus complex (see Chapter 8), and both have the same result—inability to derive satisfactory pleasure from sexual intercourse or inability to perform the sex act with a loved member of the opposite sex. For the purposes of this discussion, therefore, I shall use *impotence* to denote both male impotence and female frigidity.

Another popular fallacy concerning impotence is to blame it on sexual inhibitions imposed by our Western society. As a matter of fact, the problems of impotence are just as great or greater among primitive races. The record of history shows that these problems reached a peak in civilizations which imposed no restrictions on promiscuous sexual relationships.

The cause of impotence is deeply rooted in the subconscious. It involves the loss of ability to adjust to one of the basic human instincts, the sex act. It is a denial of the normal function of the genitals. It is psychological self-castration. Impotence cannot be "cured" by quack remedies peddled by charlatans—or even by glandular treatments prescribed by well-meaning physicians. Psychiatric treatment, as noted, can obtain effective results—but only if the patient cooperates and really wants to be cured.

Mrs. Q, age thirty-three, had been married nine years and was still a virgin. She said that although she and her husband had attempted to have sexual intercourse, whenever he started to insert his penis into her vagina the pain was so excruciating that they could not proceed. Even so, Mr. and Mrs. Q seemed devoted to each other. He nodded his head and agreed in a tender voice that he would prefer to do without intercourse than to cause his wife discomfort.

Mrs. Q, however, wanted to have a baby. After the nurse prepared her in the examining room, I started the examination to determine what, if any, physical impairment there might be to pregnancy. Immediately Mrs. Q pulled her knees together, spasmodically tightened the muscles around the vaginal opening, and with tears in her eyes wailed that I was going to hurt her. It took quite a while for the nurse and me to reassure her and gradually persuade her to relax her thighs and her genital muscles. When she finally did, I discovered that her vaginal opening was larger than that of many women who have borne several children. Her vagina could easily accommodate her husband's genital structure. All her sexual organs were perfectly normal.

Later in the consulting room I explained to Mrs. Q that she was physically capable of fulfilling her urge to bear a child, and that the pain she felt was due to the spasmodic tightening of her vaginal muscles because of her mental repressions resulting in fear. She seemed to understand the situation and said that she would try to have intercourse with her husband.

All attempts, however, were unsuccessful. Mr. and Mrs. Q would discuss the matter quite rationally while sitting in their living room. Then they would go into the bedroom and prepare to have sexual intercourse. But as soon as they got into bed together, Mrs. Q's muscles would tighten—and Mr. Q could not produce an erection because, he said, he was afraid of hurting his wife. As a matter of fact, he was as impotent as she.

During our discussions on their visits to my office, I learned something of the causes of this double impotence.

Mrs. Q was one of six children in a family whose interests were intellectual but whose income was low. Her father was big and domineering, her mother small and meek. In the close quarters of their small house, Mrs. Q could not help hearing the sounds of her parents' bedroom while they were having sexual intercourse. Anger, resentment, and fright were aroused in her by the animal-like grunts and groans that came from her father as he satisfied his lust. Her affection for her mother was mixed with contempt because of the mother's complete submissiveness to the father. Mrs. Q's love was transferred from her parents to a gentle, kind, elder brother, who looked after her during childhood. He would hold her on his lap and read to her or tell her stories, help her to get ready for school and to dress in her "Sunday best" for church, and comfort her whenever she needed it. She used to have romantic dreams about him and fantasies about bearing him a child, but the very thought of any sexual relationship with her brother in reality brought a feeling of horror.

In Mr. Q, she has found a counterpart of this brother. Her love for her husband follows the only path it knows— Electra brother-love, with plenty of open affection but a complete repression of sensual sex longings.

Mr. Q, in turn, has found in his wife the counterpart of his mother, whom he remembers with respect and affection as "a fine, upstanding, religious woman." He, too, has an unresolved Oedipus complex and can no more perform the sex act with his wife than he could with his mother. This is why he is so unnaturally complacent about the total lack of marital sex relations.

Mr. Q is gentlemanly, courteous, and affable, looking after his wife's needs and deferring to her interests. She cherishes and understands his love and returns it in kind. They enjoy a mutual interest in literature and find pleasure in each other's companionship. Theirs is a very happy relationship—as long as the sex act does not intrude.

Perhaps psychiatric treatment could help these two to readjust to a normal sex life. Because of her desire to have a child, Mrs. Q is willing to cooperate in such treatment. Mr. Q, however, resists it. He good-naturedly points out that he and his wife are considered an ideal married couple and that previous physicians have apparently regarded Mrs. Q's difficulty as an obscure physical ailment.

"Anyway," he concludes, "rather than go to all the trouble of psychiatric treatment, if my wife wants a baby, why can't she have one by artificial insemination?"

Mr. and Mrs. Q are examples of total impotence. Both have remained abnormally in love with the first love object of their childhood—Mr. Q with his mother, Mrs. Q with her brother. Their feelings of abhorrence at the idea of incestuous sex relationships persist in regard to the substitute—the wife and the husband. These individuals have a great need to give and receive love and affection—but only asexually. Their mental horror of sexual intercourse makes them impotent.

The partially impotent individual frequently marries the respected love object but is unable to have sexual intercourse with this spouse, and resorts to adultery with a member of the opposite sex who is held in contempt. Such was the case with Edmond, who came to me for treatment of a venereal disease. He was thirty at the time and had been married for ten years to a woman whom he loved with deep affection. He told me that on their honeymoon they had attempted sexual intercourse, but the results were very unsatisfactory. This he attributed to his inexperience and fear of hurting his bride.

Soon after marriage, Edmond gained more than eighty pounds, a development considered by him, his wife, and their families and friends a tribute to his wife's cooking skill. Although he has continually complained about his weight, Edmond has never seriously tried to reduce. He has used it as an excuse for not having marital sex relations, because his wife is so tiny that he fears his weight may injure her. He also adds that he is afraid of getting her pregnant, and he says they cannot afford to have children at this time. All these rationalizations, of course, are merely to cover up the fact that he is impotent with his wife, who reminds him of his mother.

Not understanding the reason for his impotence and depressed by it, Edmond welcomed an invitation to join some men from his office who were going to a local house of prostitution. It was a revelation to Edmond. He was fascinated and sexually aroused by these women whose dress, speech, and behavior were the complete opposite of his wife's or his mother's. He discovered that with these openly vulgar and suggestive women he felt an uninhibited flow of sensual pleasure and could have quite satisfactory sexual relations.

"I have no affection whatsoever for these prostitutes," he

told me. "Although it may sound like I'm lying, the truth is that these experiences make me love my wife and home all the more."

His main concern about catching a venereal disease was not about himself, but that his wife might find out about it. He did not realize that his disease actually satisfied his subconscious need for punishment to assuage his sense of guilt. In fact, partial impotents such as Edmond often try to become infected for this very reason.

The usual sequence, which will probably overtake Edmond, is a growing dissatisfaction and mental anxiety from the incompleteness of the sexual relations. The subconscious guilt feelings, which originated in the fear of incest with the first Oedipus love object, continue to demand punishment and may lead to various kinds of perversion.

Some form of masturbation is common in impotent males. A common form of disguised masturbation is prostate massage. I remember my introduction to this psychological ruse. As a young doctor just starting in practice, I conscientiously always left my number with the medical exchange service for night calls. On this particular night, I was celebrating a special occasion at a party with some friends. At 11:30 P.M. I received an emergency call from the wife of an alcoholic patient. She told me that her husband was in excruciating pain and that I must meet them at my office at once.

I rushed away from the party and found the couple waiting for me at the office. The man was literally doubled over with pain, clutching at his genitals.

"Doctor," he gasped, "I have chronic prostate trouble. I got it during the war. For years I've been going to the VA hospital, where they massage my prostate to relieve this awful pain. It's the only thing that helps me. And now it's come on me in the middle of the night! Please, Doctor, will you give me a prostate massage—quick!"

At medical school I had been taught the technique of prostate massage, which consists simply of inserting the finger into the patient's rectum and massaging his prostate gland that is located on the other side of the rectal wall, at the base of the penis. It was puzzling to me how this uncomfortable procedure could relieve the pain of which my midnight patient complained. But I wanted to make him feel better, and since he insisted this therapy had worked before and was the only thing that could possibly help him, I decided to use the procedure.

He assumed the position of placing his chest on the examining table and feet on the floor and I started massaging. At first he moaned and groaned more than ever. Then suddenly he slumped down, exclaimed, "Oh-h-h-!"—and to my amazement had an orgasm.

A few moments later he was up and putting on his pants. "Thanks, Doctor," he said. "I feel fine now."

He was one of the first patients I encountered who had to feel pain in order to punish himself subconsciously for his sexual desires. He was completely impotent for marital sex relations and had to resort to the painful treatment of prostate massage to attain sexual pleasure.

XXII

Schizo–Sex

I stopped dead in my tracks and stared at the placard. It was advertising a series of lectures on "How To Be Happy In Marriage," "Find Yourself Through Love," and "You Can Be What You Want To Be." And staring back at me, as a featured lecturer, was the photograph of my schizophrenic patient! I could not believe my eyes. But it was she, all right. The face and the name tallied. It could be no one else. It was so ludicrous that I would have burst out laughing —if it had not been so tragic. Tragic—not for my patient— but for the gullible public who would gobble up what she said.

She had come to me some weeks before with a weight problem. She tipped the scales at 219 pounds. Tightly corseted, her face expertly made up, she was not unattractive in a bizarre sort of way. But when I saw her on the examining table, bizarre was the word. Her gross, flaccid body seemed to ooze over the surface of the table. Her abdomen was mapped with scars—incisions for surgical removal of belly fat, for removal of a baby by Caesarean section, for removal of the female organs, for repair of hernia, for intestinal blockage due to adhesions.

"I think I must be abusing my body so Frances won't want to use it any more," she told me later in the consulting room.

"Frances" or "Francis"? Since the latter is a man's name, perhaps she meant her husband? I glanced at the partial history on my desk. No—his name was Edward, Edward S——. In fact, Mr. S, a social worker, had come in to make the appointment for his wife, requesting me to treat her only for her medical problem, not her mental or emotional problems. He was, he said, quite capable of handling those.

"Frances came to live in my body with me when I was only a child," Mrs. S was saying. "She died, you know. Her mother was a nun and her father was a sailor. Her mother killed herself, and Frances ran away from the nunnery when she was twelve, and lost her virginity then. Her lover killed her. But she didn't want to die, so she looked for another body. She liked mine. I wasn't so fat then.

"Sometimes it gets uncomfortable not having any privacy," she rattled on.

"I get jealous of her sometimes, though, when I think Edward is liking her better than he is me. I guess it makes it hard for him, trying to buy things for both of us and taking us out. We have such different tastes. I'm the intellectual type, but Frances likes to dance and flirt, and Frances drinks, but I don't. Yet I'm the one who's left the next day with a sick stomach and vomiting. It isn't fair!

"You know," Mrs. S's tone became confidential. "I think she does things like that because she's jealous of me—because Edward doesn't want to have sex with anybody but me. He says my body is so repulsive that it excites him sexually more than anything else in his life. He says he never wants to have intercourse with any woman in the world but me!" There was a look of sly triumph on her face. "My name is Gwynel," she added. She smoothed her hands over her corseted bulges. "And this is Gwynel's body."

I knew the weight-losing diet was doomed from the beginning. But Gwynel had been coming weekly for her appointment. She had no intention of losing a pound, but she liked to have a doctor to prattle to. Obviously it was part of her pattern to do this sort of thing at regular intervals. When she first came to me, she was taking enough sleeping pills to tranquilize a rhinoceros, but that didn't seem to faze her. I insisted, however, that she give them up. To get her to do so, I had to substitute something that was less injurious.

Her stories were characteristic of a severe mental disorder. Even on the psychiatric ward of New York's Bellevue Hospital, I had not encountered a more completely split personality (schizophrenia). As I pieced together the fragments of reality from her fantasies, I got a picture of her background —a family of twelve children, a neglectful mother whom she hatred, a nebulous father who died when she was a child, a stepfather whom she also hated, a feeling of constantly being imposed upon, and on and on.

Her repressions had been so strong and so destructive that she had subconsciously invented Frances in order to release her tensions in a manner that her conscious mind would accept. And she had fought for the existence of Frances against all comers. Her teachers, her priests, her family, had all called her a liar and punished her for her stories about this other personality who shared her body. The punishments, of course, were subconsciously welcomed as atonement for her guilty feelings of hate toward her mother and the rest of the world. If it had not been for the fantasy of Frances, this destructive hate would have turned inward against herself and Gwynel would probably have committed suicide. She had been close to it several times. Especially when she was in a destructive mood, she had an eerie way of referring to herself in the third person.

"Gwynel feels sorry for her body," she told me one day. "It takes such a beating from both Gwynel and Frances. But Frances can leave it—Gwynel can't. And Gwynel is a hypocrite like everybody else. She never lets anybody see her cry. Everybody thinks she and Edward are such an ideal couple. But sometimes Gwynel believes that Edward only uses her. It's a horrible feeling when people use you. Everybody has always used Gwynel. Frances too. Gwynel never had anything just for herself, not even her body. That's why she wants to die."

And this is the woman who is occupying a public platform to tell other people how to be happy!

Not long after I saw that first placard, Gwynel failed to come back for her appointment. Perhaps I had been advising her too strongly of her need for psychiatric help, and she was afraid she might lose Frances.

Gwynel is prospering from her lecture courses, teaching others how to achieve the good life, of which Gwynel and Edward—not to mention Frances—hold themselves up as shining examples.

Although this pair is an extreme case, there are thousands of benighted sexperts daily giving advice on sex and philosophy—projecting their own severe mental disturbances into the thinking (if one may call it that) of the unwary public.

If some in our society are already sick, should mentally ill teachers be allowed to make them sicker? Or has our society become so mesmerized by schizophrenics that it will listen to no one else?

It is certainly true that the philosophy and practice of sex as advocated by the sexperts is becoming more and more widespread, and, as a consequence, the sex life of human beings is becoming increasingly unnatural for this stage of evolution. Instead of progressing, it is retrogressing.

The most prevalent deviations of the sex act among married couples as well as free lovers are retrogressions to the oral and anal stages of infancy. As noted in earlier chapters, the infant's first sensation of pleasure is sucking milk from the mother's breast. At about the same time he experiences the pleasant relief of eliminating waste from his bladder and his bowels.

In the oral perversion of mouth-genital contact, medically referred to as fellatio and cunnilingus, the mouth of each

partner is used on the genitals of the other. In the anal perversion, anal intercourse and oral manipulation are used instead
of the genital act.

To people of normal inclinations, such perversions are disgusting. It is rather alarming, however, to note that the
abnormal is not only becoming more widely tolerated but is
even being accepted by some as normal.

Shortly after I came to Los Angeles, I began to hear rumors
about the practice of "changing partners" among groups of
married couples. It seemed unlikely that these stories were
true. I soon found out, however, that the rumors were real.

A woman patient who felt grateful toward me for the
successful removal of her appendix asked me, during a post-
operative visit to my office, if she might speak confidentially.
I assured her that she could.

She then told me that she and her husband belonged to a
group of married couples who met at regular intervals to
exchange partners for sexual intercourse. She asked me if
my wife and I would like to join the group.

I was somewhat taken aback. But being professionally
curious, I requested further information.

Mrs. S explained that when she sees her husband having
intercourse with another woman she becomes sexually stimulated herself and is a better sex partner for him afterward.
He, too, seems to enjoy watching his wife perform the sex act
with another man. They do this about every ten days in order
to get freshly stimulated for each other. When it is her turn
to perform, she stated, she gets her greatest thrill in an oral
perversion with another man while her husband looks on.

Probing further into her subconcious, I learned that Mrs. S
as a child had peeped through the keyhole to watch her
parents during their sex act and had seen her mother with her
father's penis in her mouth. She had watched this performance
several times. Subsequently she learned that her parents' deviation from more usual sexual practices was not socially acceptable.

Having a highly unresolved Electra complex toward her father, Mrs. S still subconsciously wishes to replace her mother. In the perverted sexual intercourse in which she and her husband indulged with other couples, she satisfied this Electra wish. By their enjoyment in watching each other during the sex act with another partner, both Mrs. S and her husband (as well as the other couples involved) showed a retrogression to the infantile stage of exhibitionism and voyeurism.

Mrs. S's main concern, when I politely refused her invitation, was that I not betray her confidence. In this, too, she showed a subconscious desire for punishment by expecting or wanting to be criticized. Such "wife swapping" groups are being featured on the motion-picture screen and in today's literature. The sadistic-masochistic behavior extolled in the media is echoed in daily news bulletins and headlines.

When husband and wife find a true fulfillment of their sexual needs in each other, they do not indulge in such activities. Although Mr. and Mrs. S are still married to each other now, I cannot believe that their kind of marriage is an enduring one.

I am reminded of the life story of Dutch Schultz, the notorious gangster of the 1920s, who apparently found the ideal mate toward the end of his infamous career. She lived with him as his common-law wife, attending to all his needs, including the procurement of show girls, women acrobats, and other females who appealed to him. At last, however, her real feelings showed themselves. Her apparent unselfish love of desiring to satisfy his every wish was in reality a repressed hate for his failure to be a compassionate companion. Dutch Schultz, who had evaded all attempts of his legal and illegal enemies to "get" him, was betrayed by his trusted mistress into a fatal ambush by rival gangsters.

This, to me, seems to exemplify the real feelings in the "changing partners" game. Sexual lusts relieved in this way can only defeat the natural purposes of the man-to-woman relationship and result in nothing but contempt of the partners for each other.

Throughout history, whenever women in a society are debased and degraded by men, the incidence of perversion and sexual sickness increases in direct proportion. This is as true in primitive and debased cultures today as it was in Babylon, Greece, and Rome in the past. As happened before the downfall of those ancient civilizations, some misguided "moderns" are using the increasing incidence of perversion in our own society to justify perversion. In our present Western civilization, the sexual attitude toward women has reached an all-time low—and not only are women accepting this status, but they are helping to foster it. This, I feel, is a greater threat to human survival and progress than nuclear power or space weaponry.

The slogan "Make love, not war" is an enticing idea. The love advocates must bear in mind, however, that love leading to peace must be based on mutual understanding and concern, not on carnal sex relations. Events of the past clearly show that the most completely and permanently vanquished nations are those ravaged by perverted love, not war.

XXIII

~~~~~~~~~~~~~~~~~~~~~~~~~~~~~~~~~~~

Sadism and Masochism

A cheap gold rinse on her white hair, her seamed face garish with makeup, the new patient limped into my office with one hand on a cane, the other on the arm of a neat, solicitous little man, who proved to be her husband. Mrs. W complained of aches and pains which she related to kidney trouble and high blood pressure. Her limp, she said, was the result of an automobile accident in which her hip was broken. It had healed badly, shortening her leg. Her blood pressure was high, although not unusually so for her age, and she had some evidence of kidney trouble, so I treated her for those ailments. Whenever she complained of feeling badly, Mr. W brought her to see me. He was very quiet and restrained, speaking only of his concern for his wife's health and never looking directly at anyone.

Then came a day when Mrs. W appeared with a bloody nose, a cut lip, and a black eye. Bloody urine evidenced that she had been kicked or beaten on the kidneys. To my amazement, I was informed that these injuries had been inflicted by her meek little husband in a perverted orgy of sex lust. Once the secret was out, Mrs. W confided further that he was also responsible for her broken hip and a previously fractured elbow which no longer functioned properly. She said that the only way her husband could achieve sexual pleasure was by injuring her physically. When I suggested that she take some action, legal or personal, to protect herself, Mrs. W insisted that she could not leave Mr. W because she needed him to take care of her. She abused him verbally in my presence, while he stood by silently. It was almost impossible to picture this skinny five-foot-four man, so precise in manner, aroused to such a pitch of frenzy that he possessed the strength to break his wife's bones.

From then on, Mr. W faithfully brought his wife in to be patched up after his sadistic orgies. He was meticulous in paying the bills. Mrs. W never admitted to finding any sexual pleasure in her suffering and pain, but she accepted Mr. W's sadism with the same indifference as if he had taken her to the corner drugstore to buy her a soda. She was more anxious to receive extreme sympathy from me and to tell me her life's problems than she was in being treated for her injuries. It was pathetic to see her limp in, aging and growing progressively distorted mentally and physically—but she stubbornly refused to give up this adjustment to her self-hate. Her death instincts were so strong that if her husband had not supplied her masochistic need for the perverted pleasure of pain and punishment, she would probably have destroyed herself more directly by stepping in front of a car, falling down a flight of steps, or finding some other such deliberate "accident."

Mr. W's destructive hate energies were so overwhelming in his conscious as well as his subconscious mind that he had to project them onto an outside "love object" in order to save himself from self-destruction. In both of these miserable individuals, the love channel was completely blocked—and in Mr. W's case, the eating channel was apparently used only for susbsistence. All his mental energies were therefore discharged through the hate channel, as were most of Mrs. W's. Her hate was turned inward in what is known as masochism, his outward in sadism. Conversely, the sadist may reverse the direction of his energies and become a masochist—and a masochist may become a sadist.

The "identity of opposites" is more obvious in perversions than in normal actions. In sex perversion, the struggle between the life and death instincts is manifest. It is also present in the natural sex act, but the libidinal or life instincts are so dominant that the struggle is not apparent. Even in normal sex relations, however, the elements of sadism and masochism exist in mind form. "We always hurt the one we love" is the expression of a truth which is accepted the world over. The injury, mental or physical, is usually slight and apparently unintentional, but it arises from the ever-present subconscious struggle between the life-giving force of love and the death-dealing energies of hate.

In all sex perversions, the destructive or death instincts overbalance the life instincts. Sadism and masochism are basic components of all perversions. Sadism is the compulsion to inflict physical or mental pain on others. The sadist releases guilt feelings by projecting them on others. When it is projected onto a "love object," the sadistic energy becomes eroticized and the sadist receives sexual pleasure. Enough love energies are aroused to dilute the hate, so that the love object is only injured, not murdered.

Masochism is sadism turned against oneself as the "love object." The self-hate is sufficiently neutralized by the life instincts to prevent direct suicide, but the end purpose is the same. Alcoholism and drug addiction are forms of masochism. So is melancholia. So are martydom and asceticism. Abnormal behavior of this type is manifested in various methods of mental or physical self-mutilation. The masochist is less dangerous to society then the sadist, although every masochist has the elements of sadism in his mental apparatus.

There has been a good deal of discussion recently about child abuse, which is the result of direct sadism on the part of the parent. It may be that the parent consciously or subconsciously desires to have sex relations with the child and punishes the child instead of himself or herself to atone for overwhelming guilt feelings. Abusive parents may be ab-

normally resentful of the curbs placed on their personal freedom by the necessity of caring or providing for the child, or
they may be repeating by projection their own experiences as
unloved children. As with Mr. W and his wife, after beating
or brutally using the child, the sadistic parent will try to atone
by bringing the child to a doctor with a story about an
"accident" in which the child involved himself. Unlike an
adult (such as Mrs. W) the child is usually so terrorized that
he will not betray the parent. The types of injuries, however,
usually do, and many states have now passed laws protecting
the physician in reporting such cases. For his mental as well
as his physical safety, the child should not be allowed to
remain in this type of environment.

Sadistic or masochistic behavior has no relationship to
intelligence, race, profession, sex, or economic status. The destructive instinct is inherent in everyone, everywhere. Its control is conditioned by both environment and inherited characteristics. Some individuals are born with a greater or lesser
capacity to neutralize the death instincts. The environment
may be the deciding factor as to the direction in which these
destructive energies are aimed.

Mental control of the destructive energies is handled by
the conscience, which has evolved in the human being for the
purpose of adjusting the original demands of the instincts to
conform to the physical and moral reality of the present environment. An overly developed conscience can cause as
much trouble as one that is underdeveloped. The overly
developed conscience is too repressive, the underdeveloped
conscience too permissive. Its development into balanced or
imbalanced control largely reflects the child's early training.

As mentioned earlier, there is a mild element of sadism and
masochism in all sexual relationships. Every family physician,
for example, is familiar with the type of patient known as
the bored housewife, whose visits to the doctor's office con-
stitute her only outlet for social relationships and personal
attention. Her husband is usually a sober, steady fellow, who

comes home tired from office or shop and wants to do nothing in the evening but sit around and watch television until time to go to bed, which is the only place where he enjoys a personal relationship with his wife. He can't understand why the sex act isn't as completely satisfying in her life as it is in his. He thinks her requests to go out to the movies, to visit friends, or to take a weekend trip are ridiculous. What's the matter with the woman, anyway? He provides her with a good home, equipped with the latest labor-saving devices. She gets to be with the children every day, while he only has the chance on weekends. He gives her everything—except, of course, the personal attention and social outlets which, although he does not realize it, are essential to her well-being. If anyone accused him of "mental cruelty," he would be shocked, hurt, and indignant.

His wife suffers, not always in silence but usually in vain. To release her mental stress, her subconscious projects it into a physical manifestation as a various assortment of psychosomatic ailments that may range from backache to heart trouble. These illnesses necessitate regular visits to the doctor's office, where she enjoys visiting with the secretary and other patients in the waiting room. Usually she is accompanied by her small children, who behave very well and therefore bring compliments to their mother. When her turn comes to see the doctor, the secretary or one of the nurses serves as baby-sitter—and for a brief period of time, this dutiful but bored little woman is free to be herself. The doctor is courteous and considerate, listening patiently to her own personal problem. In the examining room, she and the nurse have a cozy chat, while waiting for the doctor to join them. She always feels so much better afterward—but she always makes it a point to find some reason for having to return the following week.

Her husband can understand these expeditions. He is sincerely concerned about his wife's physical health and makes no complaint about the expense of her treatments. On occasion, when I have attempted to explain the situation to such a husband, urging him to take his wife out at least one evening a week, he is completely uncomprehending. How can a valueless thing like that affect his wife's health? As for medical expense—has he ever made a complaint? If he does grudgingly agree to try out my suggestion, his wife usually shows such a marked improvement within a month that he decides she is cured. He settles down once more to his complacent routine —and his wife soon resumes her visits to the doctor.

Every wife and mother needs to have time to herself once in a while, and at least one interval during the week when she can be alone with her husband outside the bed. To deprive her of this is a form of subconscious sadism, no matter how it may be rationalized.

XXIV

~~~~~~

Narcissism and Suicide

Greek mythology is so filled with symbolism of the sub-conscious that it is the source of many of our own terms pertaining to sex. Eros, the Greek god of love, for example, has lent his name to words denoting sensual sex—such as *erotic, eroticism, eroticize.*

Narcissism, the term for extreme self-love, derives from the Greek legend of Narcissus, the handsome young man with whom the nymph Echo fell in love. Narcissus was so vain that he could love no one but himself, and poor Echo wasted away with grief until she became a mere voice. Nemesis, the goddess of retribution, punished Narcissus by causing him to drink from a magic spring. When he saw his reflection in the mirror-like waters, Narcissus was so over-whelmed with passion for himself that he pined away, looking at his reflection, and finally died. The gods turned him into the flower that bears his name.

Modern psychiatry has used his name for the narcissist, a perverted individual whose death instincts are so abnorm-ally powerful in comparison with his life instincts that all his libidinal energies must be used with the mental apparatus itself to neutralize his destructive energies. There is no love energy left over to expend on a love object in the external world. The narcissist may marry, but the spouse is merely an echo who must repeat the narcissist's own thoughts of self-adoration. He must see the image of himself reflected in the admiration and praise he receives from others. If he looks within the mirror of his own conscience, he becomes so overwhelmed with depression and self-hate that he becomes suicidal.

The narcissist can receive sexual pleasure only in masturbation. Participation in the sex act is merely another means of masturbating, of gratifying the narcissist's love of his own body. There is no feeling whatsoever for the sex partner, who serves only as a source of additional love energy which can be absorbed into the mental apparatus of the narcissist to help neutralize his death instincts.

Though he is "selfish," "cold," and "callous," he is simply fighting for survival. If he should channel any of his love energy toward someone other than himself, he would die by his own hand under the dictates of his death instincts. The narcissist is to be pitied—and avoided.

Usually, however, he is neither pitied nor avoided. Most narcissists are remarkably good-looking and intelligent. They evoke natural admiration from others. They themselves show a preference for homely people who offer no competition—only admiration.

Dean is a typical narcissist. At thirty-one, he is a beautiful figure of a man, with classic features and rippling muscles. He has, of course, always attracted the female sex, and his road to success from his start as a moneyless high school dropout to a prosperous interior decorator's career has been paved by feminine money and favors. He has accepted all this as his due. He has never had any attachment to his admirers and no compunction about sloughing them off when they ceased to extoll his virtues as an Adonis. He has had just about as many affairs with men as he has with women. It makes no difference to Dean, since his only love is himself. He recalls having begotten four illegitimate children, but he does not remember their mothers' names or know—or care

—where they are. He just considers that these women should be grateful for having been given children by him.

To the astonishment of his coterie of followers, Dean at twenty-seven married Betty, the homely daughter of a poor family. She was completely stunned. In fact, she had been almost paralyzed with ecstasy from the moment he first started paying attention to her. Betty could not understand her good fortune. Dean had never had so fanatical a worshipper at the shrine of his own adored idol, himself. Betty made no protest when he told her that he needed all his money for his business, and could only afford to set up housekeeping in a one-bedroom shack in an offbeat section of town. To her, it was heaven.

For four years, Betty has obeyed Dean explicitly, never leaving their little house except to go to market, and to come to my office on matters pertaining to the bearing and caring for their two children. Dean frequently goes away on business trips, she says, but on every night that he spends at home they have sexual intercourse three or four times. Betty believes that Dean loves her—and until very recently, she believed that he had been true to her.

However, after his return from a month in Mexico with a client, he infected Betty with gonorrhea. Because she wanted to, she accepted his story that he got the infection from unsanitary toilet facilities. Subsequently, however, there was so much evidence of Dean's sexual involvement with women clients (the idea of his also having affairs with men never entering Betty's head), that Betty questioned him about it. Dean was furious.

As a result, he has now packed his clothes and left her. Betty is in the depths of misery. How she loves him! How can she live without him? Surely he will come back!

I have no idea that Dean will ever return. Once a worshipper has questioned this god, his subconscious fears will keep him away. He must have unquestioning adoration.

The only hope for Betty is that she can be helped to make a more normal adjustment to life, to overcome the sense of inferiority that made her such a willing slave to Dean.

There is no "cure" that I know of for a narcissist. The only time that he can be helped is as a child. If the parents can help nourish his love feelings in a realistic way and assure a normal resolution of his Oedipus complex, the narcissist stands a chance of later being able to transfer his early Oedipus love to another person and of achieving a nearly normal life. But if his Oedipus love is thrust back upon him by the parents, and he is frustrated by reality from the start, his unhappy longings will be converted into greater narcissistic energy.

I have seen an unusual type of narcissism manifested in some cases of mental illness. When the mental patient becomes physically ill, especially when surgery is required, he becomes mentally well. The extreme physical stimulation of the operation or serious illness produces energies from the external world which his mental apparatus uses to bind the uncontrolled instinctual energies and project them onto pain-focused parts of his body, such as the surgical scar. The tremendous tensions that caused the mental illness are released, at least temporarily, and the patient comes in touch with reality.

In the normal individual, a certain amount of libidinal energy is always used to neutralize the destructive instincts and maintain the natural balance of self-love and self-hate. It is the proportion of the love energies required to neutralize the death instincts that determines normality or abnormality. The individual with an abundance of libidinal energy has a great deal left over to channel into the external world. The individual with less of these life-supporting energies has to conserve a larger percentage for himself in order to survive.

In the narcissist, the life and death forces are balanced on such a thin edge that a single event can tip the scales from extreme self-love to extreme self-hate and suicide. One reads in the news about a woman who took poison because her husband left her or a man who shot himself because of disastrous business reverses. The events cited were not the real causes. The death instincts in these people were so strong that the outside incident in each case supplied the last bit of destructive energy necessary to overwhelm the conscious mind beyond its power of repression. Once these energies entered the conscious mind, it was compelled to discharge them, and the only release for pleasure in these cases was in the ultimate peace of death.

Many deaths reported as accidents are really disguised suicides. The *Los Angeles Times* reported this example.

An Oxnard man was killed Friday while riding in a car being operated by the same woman whose erratic driving three days earlier had caused him to be cited for letting her drive without a license or a learner's permit.

The subconscious death wish in this man was so strong that when it was not fulfilled in the first attempt, a second was made almost immediately and with success.

Opposition increases the intensity of any instinct. The challenge of adversity—if it is not overwhelming—whets the instincts of mastery and self-determination. If these survival instincts have little or no opposition, they do not develop to full strength—just like a muscle that is not exercised. This no doubt is a contributing factor in cases of narcissism, which usually occurs in people to whom others naturally cater.

I believe this is a likely cause of the high suicide rate in Sweden. Physically handsome as a people, in the widely admired blonde, blue-eyed tradition, and highly developed intellectually, the Swedes are well accepted everywhere. They meet little or no resistance in the form of prejudice or discrimination. Their own society permits great freedom in sexual love. Their survival instincts have not had to be exercised in combatting these challenges which others must meet in our present society. Therefore the libidinal energies are weaker in proportion to the normal destructive energies.

In contrast, the Jews have had to combat all of these factors

to win social and even physical survival. Therefore their
destructive instincts have been suppressed at the roots, and
their survival instincts have been greatly strengthened. Their
love energies have been traditionally channelled to spouse and
family. Consequently, the suicide rate among the Jewish
people is very low.

These factors might well be worth consideration in current
studies on the alarming increase in suicides among promiscuous young people in our society.

XXV

~~~~~~~~~~~~~~~~~~~~~~~~~~~~~~~~~~~~

Homosexuality

A woman shall not wear that which pertaineth unto
a man, neither shall a man put on a woman's
garments.

—MOSES' LAW

The homosexual is in a category between narcissism and
normality. The ratio of the libidinal energies to the destructive
energies is higher than in the narcissist, but it never reaches
normal proportions. The variations in this ratio determine the
degrees of homosexuality, *i.e.*, the preference of the individual
for sex relations with a member of the same sex rather than
the opposite sex. These fall into three main classifications.

1. The 100 percent homosexual has only enough love
energy left over—after neutralizing his or her destructive
energies—to project onto an external love object of the same
sex. With identical genital anatomy, the love object becomes
a sort of glorified self-image. It is almost like loving one's
own body and therefore does not require too great a projection of libidinal energy. There is a revulsion against the
opposite sex because of the subconscious fear that a fatal
amount of libidinal energy will be demanded.

2. The ambisexual individual can enjoy sexual relations

with the opposite sex when environmental conditions are relatively undisturbed. However, under conditions of stress more libidinal energy must be retained in the self, and the amount left over is not sufficient to sustain heterosexual relations. During these periods, there is a withdrawal from and even hostility to the opposite sex. After the pressure is removed and the environment again becomes tranquil, normal sex relations may be resumed. These homosexual intervals produce varying degrees of shame, self-reproach, and feelings of guilt in the ambisexual individual. Paradoxically, if these self-created tensions become too great, the individual is driven back into homosexuality—or, if he resists this tendency, into suicide or a slower method of self-destruction such as alcoholism. In my experience, many cases of severe alcoholism have their roots in this type of homosexuality.

3. The almost normal individual, who finds pleasure in natural heterosexual relations, resorts to homosexuality only under extreme circumstances which deprive him or her of contact with the opposite sex. In such cases, the perversion is induced by abnormal conditions in the environment such as prison life, war, long expeditions, institutional isolation from the opposite sex, social or religious taboos, and the like. Children and adolescents who are sent away to private schools which admit only members of the same sex—such as military academies and girls' finishing schools—are prematurely subjected to this abnormal type of environment, and may develop homosexual tendencies.

A child whose upbringing is primarily in charge of adults of the same sex is more inclined to become a homosexual in adult life. A boy who grows up with his father in a predominantly male environment, without a significant mother influence, will feel uncomfortable in female company and be more drawn to male companions. A girl brought up by her mother, in a family of women without male influences, will feel unduly comfortable with members of her own sex and may find the opposite sex unattractive.

The determining factor in homosexual behavior, however, is always the ratio of libidinal energies to destructive energies in the mental apparatus. It is an abnormal survival adjustment. In the 100 percent homosexual, these abnormal sexual relations are accepted as perfectly normal. There is no feeling of embarrassment, shame, or guilt. In fact, the natural sex act is usually regarded with disgust.

In the ambisexual type, the homosexual tendency may remain dormant for years, until it is activated by a crisis in the environment which disturbs the uneasy balance between the life and death instincts. This is what happened to Edith when she was seventeen. At her father's insistence she came to "talk it over" with me, because as the family physician I had known her since her childhood.

Edith had been an attractive and intelligent child, who appeared normal in every way. She had been a "daddy's girl" since she was about five years old, in a smooth transition from the babyhood attachment to her mother into a natural Oedipus feeling toward her father. He, however, was an extremely strict and overbearing man, often unduly critical of his daughter's behavior. Edith reacted with conflicting emotions. She loved her father, but she resented his criticisms and in revenge would often deliberately challenge his authority by misbehaving. After her two brothers were born in close succession, Edith staunchly maintained that she was Father's favorite, but she could not help showing that she considered the boys rivals for both parents' affection.

It was the puritanical father, however, who was divorced by his charming and intellectual wife when Edith was seventeen. Although the mother was given custody of the children, Edith maintained her loyalty to her father, insisting that he was the one who had been wronged and begging to be allowed to go live with him. Then came the great shock. The father married another woman who was pregnant by him, and in four months their baby was born.

Edith felt betrayed and abandoned. Her childhood Electra

wish to replace her mother with her father had been stimulated by the divorce of her parents. Now she felt, subconsciously, that her father had been adulterous *not to her mother
but to her.* Her sense of rejection was so great that all affection for her father was withdrawn and replaced by a consuming desire for revenge.

These emotional disturbances and the increased strength of
her destructive energies threw Edith back into the pre-Electral
love stage for her mother, with a subconscious longing to return to the protective warmth and security of her mother's
breast. She fell in love with an older woman who was much
like her mother—attractively feminine, charming, intellectual,
and not too concerned about Edith. Edith played the masculine role in this affair, bringing gifts to her new love,
seeking her company, taking her out.

Edith's father was utterly horrified. That his daughter
should become a homosexual truly dismayed him. He criticized her mercilessly, argued, and threatened. The more he
stormed, the more Edith's desire for revenge was satisfied. To
defy him further, she moved into her woman lover's apartment to live.

In her discussion with me, Edith showed no interest in
changing her homosexual way of life. She found pleasure in
her paramour's companionship and affection and in their sexual relationship. She had made a sexual adjustment in which
she felt happy and comfortable and which to her seemed quite
normal. She only wanted to be left alone to enjoy it.

In making the gesture of seeking medical help, Edith was
saying, in effect, "All right, I've tried. I understand my problem, but I cannot be cured. Now I am absolved from any
further obligation to change. Now, leave me alone!"

Even in a physical illness, the patient's cooperation is important. In the case of a mental problem, it is essential. Edith
was quite right. If she didn't want to be cured, she couldn't
be.

Very few cases of female homosexuality reach the doctor's

office. Female homosexuals—called Lesbians, from the Greek island of Lesbos which was the home of Sappho, a famous poet and female ambisexual in ancient times—are more readily accepted by society. They seem to be more quietly satisfied with their life pattern and are not so obvious or ostentatious as male homosexuals.

In both male and female, homosexual behavior represents a subconscious mental and emotional regression to infantile mother love and self-love. This is why, although seeking a partner with the same sex organs as his or her own, most homosexuals of either sex identify themselves as women and prefer partners with feminine characteristics and mannerisms. Although one or the other usually assumes what might be termed the masculine role in the courtship and often in responsibilities of the household, they both regard themselves as women.

In sex relationships, most Lesbians revert to the oral stage. Male homosexuals may use oral or anal perversions or masturbate each other.

The third type of homosexuality, which becomes expressed as behavior only under extreme conditions, is quite prevalent. A subconscious fear of homosexual tendencies haunts most alcoholics, such as Billy. Now fifty-two, Billy arrives at my office on a fairly regular monthly schedule to get sobered up from a binge. He wants to be treated for his acute alcoholism, and insists that "it will never happen again." But it always does.

Billy grew up in a strict household, with parents who spent much of their time in church and school activities, leaving Billy in care of his older brother. Billy's Oedipus feelings therefore became abnormally attached to this brother.

At fourteen, Billy ran away from home, traveled around the country as a hobo, and finally found work that he liked around the racetracks. By the time he was twenty-three, he had become a trainer, and before long his horses started winning. Just as he was about to become a real success, Billy started drinking heavily and lost most of his money betting on the wrong horses. He left the racetracks and got a job as a traveling salesman. Billy still likes to brag about his sexual capacity in those days, when he would pick up a streetwalker or her equivalent in every town.

He was twenty-eight before he married a chaste young society woman, whom he greatly admired and respected. However, his genital organs would not function in the company of hers. He projected his frustrations onto her in bitter reproaches and quarrels. After every unsuccessful attempt to perform the sex act with his wife, Billy would try to drown his impotence in a prolonged drinking bout. His brother would always have to be sent for to sober him up. Then would follow a period of remorse and self-criticism.

Although Billy's wife has not left him, the repetition of this pattern has so embittered her that she, too, has developed an alcoholic problem. At one time Billy actually stayed sober for six months, and thought he had "licked the devil alcohol." He went on a lecture tour to tell about his victory, under the auspices of a church group. Remembering his former prowess, he picked up a young lady in the hotel and invited her to his room. To his complete disgust, he found that he was impotent with her, too. He rushed from the room to the nearest bar and went on a three-week drunk, which only stopped when his brother found him and brought him to me for care and hospitalization. He swore, as usual, that he was cured this time.

Billy's unresolved Oedipus complex toward his brother and his latent homosexuality have made him impotent for normal sex relations. His early attempts with streetwalkers did not satisfy his sex needs, and the frustration heightened his subconscious longing for his brother's love. Getting drunk assures him of his brother's attention. So far as I know, Billy has suppressed his homosexual feelings all his life, but he can no longer respond to the opposite sex, even to a "loose woman."

Occasionally a worried male patient will confide in me that although he would never think of having sexual relationships with anyone but a woman, he sometimes catches himself wondering if men find him attractive and how it would feel to be attracted to a man. Such thoughts are a perfectly natural manifestation of intellectual curiosity. As conscious thoughts, they are under control of the conscious mind, and they cannot get one into difficulties unless they are deliberately and knowingly acted upon. It is the subconscious which can play tricks on us. It disguises longings and antagonisms that we would refuse to accept consciously.

It was one of these tricks of the subconscious in Kenneth's mind that brought Margaret to my office with a black eye. But the bruise went much deeper. They had been out to a party the night before with their usual crowd, and there were the usual harmless, socially accepted light flirtations, which normally stimulate a young husband and wife to enjoy each other when they get home and go to bed.

Kenneth, however, had been nagging Margaret lately about Jim, the husband in a couple who were good friends of theirs. Jim was quite handsome and Margaret liked him, but she was in love with Kenneth and never gave anyone else a serious thought. Last night Kenneth had acted unreasonably jealous, had made all sorts of accusations on the way home, and after they came in had worked himself up into a violent rage and struck her. It was not the blow that hurt as much as the injustice of the whole attack.

Kenneth was now remorseful and wanted to talk to me.

Normal jealousy is a fear of losing a loved one and the sadness that will follow, combined with a feeling of guilt and wounded pride at not being able to retain the loved one's affection. Most people recognize it as an unwarranted anxiety and repress it. Or, if it is expressed and one is reassured that the fears and doubts are unfounded, it is forgotten.

Margaret's account of Kenneth's actions made me feel that his jealousy was abnormal. And it was. As it turned out and as he finally realized to his dismay, he was not jealous of Margaret's fancied interest in Jim—but the fact that Jim was flirting with Margaret instead of with Kenneth himself.

Kenneth's mother had died when he was two, and he and his older sister were brought up by their father. Kenneth's Oedipus love, which would normally have been directed toward his mother, was transferred to his father. He developed a possessive attachment to his father, and was intensely jealous whenever his sister received attention from the parent. When Kenneth was fourteen, he met a young man with whom he indulged in homosexual sex play. He admitted that he remembered this at the party when Jim and Margaret were dancing together, and he imagined how Margaret would have felt if she were having an affair with Jim. Subconsciously, however, his latent homosexual feelings were aroused toward Jim, and these in turn brought on guilt feelings of being unfaithful to Margaret. Disguising themselves as jealousy because of her behavior, all these tensions were released by Kenneth in projecting his own desires and guilt feelings onto his wife.

Homosexuality, open or latent, does not have a physical origin and it has no relationship to intellect or ethical culture. The problem exists from civilized statesmen all the way to the most primitive of savages. Because the death instinct is common to all living creatures, homosexuality occurs in all animals who reproduce by mating. It is a problem of the mental apparatus.

The hermaphrodite, in contrast to the homosexual, is the result of a strictly physical anomaly. This name also comes from Greek mythology—the legend of Hermaphroditus, the son of Hermes and Aphrodite, who grew together with the nymph Salmacis.

The hermaphrodite may be a man whose sex organs are predominantly male but contain remnants of the female organs. Or it may be a woman whose sex organs are predominantly female but have vestiges of the male genitals.

These anomalies result from incomplete development of the embryo. In the early stages of pregnancy, the new human being that is being formed in the womb has no sex organs. After the cells differentiate to build different structures of the body, a stage is reached for formation of the genitals. At first these are identical in every embryo, containing the elements of both male and female. Then further differentiation normally takes place. If the human is to become a male child, the rudiments of the female organs disappear and the male organs develop. For a female child, the reverse occurs.

Occasionally, however, the process of genital development is arrested before or during the time that the sex organs are being differentiated, and the baby is born with structures common to both sexes. The most frequent deformities are a remnant of the female vagina in the male, and in the female an abnormally large clitoris, which is a remnant of the male penis. There are many variations of hermaphroditism. Sometimes the condition can be corrected by surgery or hormone treatment.

The actual sex of the individual is determined by the fully developed male or female organs. If these structures are normal and the remnants of the other sex organs do not physically interfere, the hermaphrodite is perfectly capable of a normal sex life. Their peculiar anatomy does not make them either homosexual or ambisexual.

XXVI

Exhibitionism and Voyeurism

The perversions of exhibitionism and voyeurism are a very close-knit pair of opposites. The exhibitionist derives perverted sexual pleasure from exhibiting or displaying his genital anatomy to others. The voyeur (the French word for "viewer" or "looker") is sexually excited by seeing the sex organs and intimate acts of others. Generally these two perversions are combined. The exhibitionist is also a voyeur, and the voyeur or "Peeping Tom" is often also an exhibitionist. These perverts have regressed to a very early stage of childish sexual development. Nudist colonies are the most obvious example of the regression of adult sexuality to this infantile stage.

As previously noted, an infant's first intellectual curiosity concerns his own anatomy and that of others. Small children enjoy exposing their bodies or seeing others in the nude. Theirs is a perfectly normal or "innocent" pleasure, when they giggle and laugh during their baths and enjoy running around without any clothes on. If the parents are neither unduly prudish nor unduly immodest, children progress naturally from this early stage and learn normal modesty by example.

However, parents who lack a normal amount of modesty and persist in walking about nude overly excite the child to see nudity and exhibit his own anatomy. At the opposite extreme, parents who are overly prudish and create a feeling of shame at a normal display of anatomy unduly arouse the child's curiosity and stimulate his instinct for mastery in a desire to see and do what is forbidden. Either extreme may distort the child's normal sexual development.

A child may become permanently arrested in the exhibitionist-voyeur stage if he is seduced by an adult who derives sensual pleasure from exhibiting his anatomy to the child or viewing the child's anatomy. The sense of sight becomes eroticized, and the love energies are abnormally released through this channel.

As with all perversions, exhibitionism-voyeurism has its component of sadism-masochism. The exhibitionist-voyeur is usually a masochist, whose feelings of shame and guilt direct his hate energies against himself. He finds additional satisfaction in the derision, abuse, and punishment which others heap upon him.

Such was the case of John, who was frequently beaten up by men in rest rooms when he was caught peeping over the toilet enclosures in lustful observation or in washrooms where he freely exposed his own genitals to others.

Now under psychiatric treatment, John reminisces longingly of the days in the old swimming hole where he and his family sported in the nude. He remembers that when he was quite young, he and his brother used to peep into their parents' bedroom, deriving great interest and a sense of satisfaction from the sight of their undressed parents. Occasionally they could observe the act of intercourse.

When John was eight years old, an adult widowed cousin came to live with his family, sharing John's bedroom. Under her guidance, he attempted to participate in the adult sex act during his parents' absence. One day they returned unexpectedly and saw what was going on. The parents reacted with disgust and severity. The cousin was banished from the house, and John was emphatically conditioned from then on as to the sinfulness of the sex act. At the time, of course, he had no real adult sex inclinations and the suppression of the sex act was unimportant to him. However, it became indelibly implanted in his conscience that sensual pleasure from seeing was more acceptable to his parents than pleasure from the sex act.

In early adolescence John began to masturbate, as most boys do. However, it increased rather than relieved his tensions, because of his fear that his parents would discover him in the act. He became further distressed when he was told by friends as well as older authorities that masturbating would make him go "crazy."

As he grew older, John had a desire to see people's genitals and expose his own to them. This was when he began frequenting public rest rooms. He was finally arrested for exposing his sex organs to some children playing on the school grounds and was remanded to the psychiatric clinic.

Such cases are difficult to rehabilitate, because the roots of this perversion go so deeply into the childhood background. However, John is making good progress in responding to reason and in learning to control his behavior. Eventually it may be possible for his sexual instincts to find release in a more natural way.

The exhibitionist-voyeur is perverted primarily by factors in his early environment—unlike the narcissist and homosexual, who are born with a deficiency of libidinal energies. However, homosexuals often become exhibitionists. They thrive in such nightclubs as Finocchio's in San Francisco's North Beach, where they can gratify all aspects of their perversion. They are able to live openly as homosexuals, exhibit themselves, receive punishment through subconscious shame and open ridicule from some of the audience, project hate on the belittling customers, admire themselves dressed up in feminine finery, and be admired by other perverts—and at the same time get paid for it all.

The fact that they are paid and that such shows are profitable would seem to indicate a latent voyeurism in the apparently normal, average persons who comprise much of the audience. No one under eighteen, of course, is admitted. And yet millions of children and young teen-agers are exposed daily to films which are equally perverted and damaging to their normal sexual development.

XXVII

Other Perversions

Adult sex has no part in a normal child's life. Premature participation in the genital sex act may result in hysteria, neurosis, nymphomania, and even psychosis (serious mental illness). If the traumatic experience is repressed—eliminated from the conscious mind but stored in the subconscious—it may later exert pressure on the conscious mind and produce tensions. If the premature sex experiences are not repressed but remain in the conscious mind, the individual may become "sexually kaleidoscopic"—indulging in a variety of abnormal sex acts without normal feelings. He may repeat first one, then another stage of sexual development, or limit sexual activities to only one stage. His sex life has no mature meaning but remains distorted and confused.

Nymphomania

Nymphomania, the obsessive compulsion in women to have almost continuous sexual intercourse with men, is the result of the premature introduction of a girl child to the adult genital sex act. Nymphomania is not promiscuity in the usual sense, although the two are often confused. Some deluded men think that all women are nymphomaniacs, and most men think that it would be wonderful if they were—but my clinical experience tells me that such a morbid and un-controllable desire for sexual intercourse is not normal in women. The nymphomaniac's appetite for sex is like the alcoholic's for liquor. She can never get enough, she is never satisfied, and she gets no pleasure from it. It may destroy her and her family, but she cannot stop.

Betty B, an attractive thirty-two-year-old woman, married, with three children, is a typical nymphomaniac.

Betty's seduction began almost in babyhood, when her father used to stroke her genitals to quiet her and put her to sleep at night. She had two older brothers; a cranky, scolding mother, who was generally obnoxious to everyone; and a father who was an open woman chaser. At the age of six, Betty engaged in genital sex play with her older brother, and at eight she was having intercourse with the younger brother. Her father, aware of these relationships, not only condoned them but began to participate himself when his daughter was ten. Soon afterward, however, he deserted the family. Betty, then eleven, was sent to live with an aunt and uncle, and immediately started having intercourse with her thirteen-year-old cousin whenever his parents were away.

During her teens, Betty had sexual relations with various schoolmates. She continued the habit with other men after she left school. Up to this time, her male partners were merely the means of attempting to satisfy an insatiable sensual appetite. There was no affection involved. From infancy, her genital organs had become the focus of sensual pleasure, and she had developed no other erotic zones on her body for the relief of tension.

Then at the wedding of a relative, Betty met a man with whom she fell in love. They were married and moved to another city. Betty did her best to remain chaste. Although she enjoyed a very active sexual life with her husband, he could not fulfill her almost incessant need for intercourse, and she had several secretive affairs while he was at work. Such outlets became more and more limited as the family increased and Betty had to devote her time to the care of her children. She wanted very much to be a good mother.

With the decrease of her extramarital sexual activities, however, Betty's mental tensions built up to the point of hysteria, which was manifested as psychosomatic illness. By the time her third child was a year old, Betty had developed such severe pain in her pelvis that the doctor, who was then treating her, recommended a hysterectomy. The surgical removal of her uterus, however, only made her condition worse. She became an invalid, too weak to move from her bed without support. Her oldest child took over management of the household. For two years Betty was "too exhausted" and "felt too miserable" to do anything except eat, have intercourse with her husband, and be carted from one doctor to another.

Suddenly Betty snapped out of her hysterical state. She told her astonished husband that she "felt fine" and wanted to go downtown with some women friends that evening. Mr. B, delighted at this miraculous recovery, readily agreed. Betty stepped out to a bar, where she picked up a man and had a lusty affair in a motel. Pretty soon she was going out with "the girls" four or five nights a week. Mr. B, a hard-working man who came home tired in the evening, had neither the inclination nor the extra funds to join her, even though he discovered that she and "the girls" were enjoying some of the nightclubs. He did not suspect the truth, especially as Betty's lust for the sex act with him increased to dismaying proportions. Whenever he demurred about her going out at night, she became ill and vindictive, taking to her bed and again becoming neglectful of the house and the children.

At last, Mr. B learned that his wife was "having an affair." At first he was inconsolable, but she managed to convince him that it was an unusual situation and would not happen again. She merely wanted to get out of the house, have a drink, and dance a bit for recreation. Mr. B wanted to believe her, but when she began staying out all night, time after time, he realized that he had to do something. Since he could not control her, he decided to join her. They would, he said, step out together three nights a week.

His first time, however, proved to be his last. Mr. B bought a complete new outfit—suit, shirt, shoes—on credit, got all dressed up, called a cab, and proudly started out with his wife to meet her gay friends. He began to get excited about the prospect of seeing a good floor show, having a few drinks, dancing with his pretty wife. This would be fun! Why hadn't he done it before?

When the cab pulled up to the address Betty had given, Mr. B got his first shock. This was no glamorous night club. It was a dump, squeezed in between dingy buildings in a tough part of town. He groped his way behind Betty through the smelly semidarkness to a small table near the wooden slab of dance floor, where couples were jammed together like sardines in a can. Men in dirty sweat shirts, smoking cigars, were clutching frowsy women and wiggling to the blaring music.

Speechless, Mr. B listened dazedly while Betty ordered their drinks. Before the waiter returned, a young tough sauntered up to the table.

"Hi Betty," he greeted familiarly. "Let's dance." As she rose, he glanced over her shoulder at Mr. B and added, "Buddy, I'm dancing with your girl—and you'd better not have any objections." And off they went.

In my office the next afternoon, Mr. B stuttered out his story. His hands were trembling, his face was clammy, and his body jerked uncontrollably in the chair by my desk.

"D-doctor," he stammered, "I—I knew my w-wife was g-going out w-with other m-men—b-but good Lord! I th-thought she pr-perferred somebody who had more t-to offer than m-me. I—I w-wouldn't have m-minded so m-much if these g-guys were—well, rich b-businessmen or p-professional men or b-better than m-me in s-some way. B-b-but

these g-guys—how c-could she?" Poor Mr. B was in a state
of emotional panic and shock. My sympathies went out to
him.

Betty had not come home with him the night before.
When he had "come to" after the first jolt and wanted to
leave, she had refused to go. She had practically shoved the
dazed Mr. B into a cab and sent him packing. She herself
did not come home until late the following morning. Finding her husband in such a state of panic and depression,
she had attempted to console him by having intercourse
with him.

Betty told me that she was "awfully tired." She and her
young tough had gone to a motel where they spent the night
and morning in an incessant sexual orgy including both
normal and perverse sexual acts. She felt no remorse—only
regret that her husband was upset, and that the fulfillment
of her sexual needs took so much time from her domestic
duties at home.

To the nymphomaniac, there is nothing moral or immoral
about sexual relations. Sexual activity merely fulfills a compulsive urge. Beginning with her father's caressing of her
genitals as a baby, Betty's early experiences had been
devastating to the development of a mature sexuality. Her
father's perverted acts toward her during her childhood gave
her a distorted idea of the perfect man. Any man who would
have sexual intercourse with her was her ideal. Sexual reality
to Betty—as to any nymphomaniac—consisted of going
through incessant motions of the sex act, nothing more.
Although she tried to adjust herself to a normal life with a
loving husband and children, such a life was too foreign
to her earlier experiences. To her, the normal was so abnormal
that it brought on a hysterical breakdown, which was only
"cured" when she returned to her own bizarre reality. The
masochistic-sadistic component of her perversion was satisfied
by the punishment of mental pain and disgrace which she
brought upon herself and her family.

Satyriasis

Satyriasis is often mistakenly believed to be "the male equivalent of nymphomania." There is no male equivalent of nymphomania. The nymphomaniac does not require any feeling of sensual lust to engage in genital relations. She can do it any time, anywhere. The male, regardless of how many times he indulges in the sex act, cannot do it without having an erection, and must obtain a certain lustful satisfaction in an orgasm. Nymphomania is a perversion. Satyriasis is not.

The satyric has a need for sexual intercourse much more frequently than the average man does. He is not abnormal any more than the man who is seven feet tall. Just as the seven-foot basketball player is "taller than average," the satyric might be said to be "sexier than average." His mental tensions rebuild more rapidly than most men's do after the release in an orgasm.

It is an overwhelming amount of psychical (or mental) energy that produces satyriasis. This overabundance of psychical energy may be related to mental illness, but the sex act by which the satyric releases it is normal. He cannot perform it without an erection, and he cannot release it without an orgasm. If he cannot find a willing female partner, he may resort to indiscriminate romances for the purpose of having intercourse. But he is not a "sex maniac," in the sense that his sex act is abnormal and without gratification.

Fetishism

Fetishism is the use of a symbolic object or a nonsexual part of the body instead of the genitals as a source of sensuous sexual pleasure. A fetishist, for example, may be impotent for having sexual relationships with a loved one, but is overwhelmed with sexual pleasure at the sight or touch of the loved one's undergarments. The feet and hair are common fetishes, also a ring or chain or similar object which has belonged to the loved one.

Although normal people often cherish personal objects as romantic symbols of love, these objects are merely reminders of the loved one and not substitutes for the sex act.

To the fetishist, however, it is the symbol or fetish itself which becomes eroticized and arouses extreme sexual excitation. In a normal man, for example, the sight of a brassiere may arouse memories of the female breast, and the thought of the breast might arouse memories of the genital sex act —but the brassiere and the memories are not substitutes for the real thing. In the fetishist, however, to whom the undergarment is a symbolic substitute, the brassiere itself produces an erection—yet he is unable to perform the natural sex act and relies on masturbation after being stimulated by his fetish to have an orgasm.

Psychoanalysis substantiates Freud's diagnosis of fetishism, especially in the male as being related to the early castration complex in young children. As previously discussed, the castration complex is a subconscious fear of castration associated with Oedipus guilt feelings, causing the child to misinterpret punishments for bedwetting, thumbsucking, and examining his genitals as threats of castration. If such punishments are too severe and if the parental authority is too critical of the child's sensuous gratifications, these unrealistic subconscious fears remain unresolved and block normal release of lust feelings when the child grows up.

Even during the normal resolution of these fears, young children frequently go through the stage of cutting or pulling out their hair, using it as a subconscious protective fetish. The cutting of the hair is a painless process and temporary, since it grows back, but it serves as a subconscious sacrificial substitute for the genitals in atonement for guilt related to Oedipal lust feelings. A similar subconscious feeling may account for the preoccupation with the hair during adolescence.

The foot has symbolically represented the female genitals since antiquity. This fetish was the theme of one of Louis Nizer's stories in his book *My Life in Court*, which concerned a man who demanded the use of his wife's feet to release his sex urges.

The Reformer

The "Reformer," who tries to convert the prostitute to the straight and narrow way of life before having intercourse with her, has formed the subject of many famous novels and films (*Rain, Elmer Gantry, Never on Sunday*). He is the incongruous but not uncommon result of a certain type of unresolved Oedipus complex.

Joe, for example, is a good-looking and successful businessman. The only son of an upstanding father and a righteous but overly possessive mother, to whom he has been extremely attached all his life, Joe is now in middle age. He has never married, but has had numerous affairs with married women. His recent affair with Sally is typical.

Joe met Sally about six months ago at a dinner party given by a member of his firm. Although apparently happily married, she was a flirt. Joe was attracted to her, but his interest became really aroused later when he learned from someone in the office that Sally had been involved in a scandal before her marriage, and that she was generally considered to be "lively and loose." He began to daydream about her and at night to dream of her with such vivid sensuousness that he often woke up and had to masturbate. When he learned that she and her husband were going to attend another social affair to which he had been invited, Joe could hardly wait.

He exerted all his experienced charm, which was considerable, in seducing her. He romanced her with unwavering gallantry and devotion. When she finally came to his apartment, he provided the perfect setting with candlelight, wine, and soft music. When the evening culminated in bed, however, Joe did not make passionate love to Sally. Lying beside her, he regaled her with a long dissertation on the evils of her having intercourse with anyone but him. He did not want her to divorce her husband, but merely to stop having marital sexual relations. As to extramarital affairs —except with Joe—Sally must mend her ways and save herself before she ruined her life. If she would let him, he would help her to develop the character to remain true to herself and him. At last, he demonstrated the joy they could have together.

Their affair went along very satisfactorily in this manner until Sally divorced her husband. Immediately Joe "divorced" Sally. He lost all interest in her and found no pleasure in her company. Soon after he broke off relations with Sally, Joe met an older married woman in a dance hall and another affair began.

Throughout his adult life, in one affair after another, Joe has been reliving his unresolved Oedipus attachment to his mother. Her overly possessive attitude toward him caused his childhood fantasies to persist past the normal stage into his youth. When he learned about promiscuous women and prostitutes, his fantasies and dreams incorporated this knowledge. He was still the noble knight, who rescued the fair damsel, his mother, as in his childhood dreams—but he was also many lovers in disguise having affairs with his mother in the disguised form of a prostitute. His subconscious continued to identify his mother's sexual relations with his father as the most flagrant infidelity to himself.

Many times his dreams were so sensuously vivid that he awakened with a wet dream. Then he discovered that he could release his lust feelings in real life with the prostitutes of the community, but these were imperfect mother substitutes. He found the ideal subconscious mother substitute in a promiscuous older married woman whose husband became the subconscious stand-in for his father. By getting his paramour to abstain from the marital sex act, Joe satisfied his subconscious vengeance on his father. By his sermons and attempts to reform his paramour before the culmination of the seduction, Joe was reenacting the noble deed by which the knight earned the favor of his lady love. If she really "reformed," however, or became divorced, she more realistically represented his mother—and Joe immediately became impotent for the sex act. The pattern of the affair must always follow that of his lust fantasies, with loose women symbolically standing in for his mother.

With the "Reformer," such as Joe, the sex act itself is normal, but the reality in which he becomes potent is abnormal. When his paramour disturbs this abnormal reality, she is sadistically punished by being abandoned

Prevention of perversions is far better than any treatment. The best way to avoid disturbances of sexuality is to prevent them from developing during childhood. For a child's normal growth, it is as essential to attend to his sex needs in a suitable manner as it is to see that he has the proper food, clothing, and shelter.

Parents readily recognize how harmful it would be to feed a young child highly seasoned food and alcoholic beverages instead of body-building proteins and pure water. Yet it is even more injurious to provide him with sensual stimuli that his young mind has no need for and cannot handle.

XXVIII

~~~~~~~~~~~~~~~~~~~~~~~~~~~~~~~~~~

Child-Molesters

Why is the incidence of the rape of children so much greater today than ever before in history? Although all forms of perversion seem to be increasing, there is a very high rate of increase in the number of perverts who have an erotic craving for children, and who require a child in order to reach maximum sensual release in an orgasm. It has been estimated that in Sing Sing prison, for example, two-thirds of all sex criminals are those who commit sexual offenses against children. Of course, not all child-molesters are discovered and jailed.

The pedophile, or child-molester, is regarded with disgust and horror by all normal people. Even hardened prisoners, who tolerate murderers and other perverts, will not associate with the pedophile, but hold him in scornful contempt. The child-molester is on the bottom rung of the pervert society's ladder.

My personal clinical experience leads me to classify this perversion among those caused primarily by premature sexual experiences in childhood. This theory is supported by the findings of Dr. Ralph Slovenko, whose book *Social Behavior and the Law* reports on his study of Sing Sing inmates imprisoned for sex crimes. Dr. Slovenko concludes that early psychosexual training and experience have arrested the pedophile in an immature stage of sexual development, preventing him from making a normal sexual adjustment.

The child-molester might be called a "kaleidoscopic pervert." He may require either a male or a female child for his sexual gratification. The sexual act with the child may consist of genital intercourse, anal intercourse (sodomy), fellatio, exhibitionism, voyeurism, masturbation, or a combination of any of these. Some pedophiles, for example, masturbate themselves while exposing their own anatomy or examining or using the child's body.

The child-molester is, in one way or another, reenacting the sexual abuse or seduction inflicted upon him as a child. He usually has a fear of adults, perhaps as a result of his early traumatic experience. He has a feeling of inferiority, associated with guilt and dislike of himself. To neutralize his instinct for self-destruction, he turns his libidinal energies inward in a form of narcissism, and bolsters his instinct of mastery by his feeling of dominance over a child. His masochistic need for punishment is often satisfied by allowing himself to be abused and taken advantage of by children, toward whom he may at first assume a benevolent and patronizing air. Then the sadistic component asserts itself in physical abuse or attack on the child victim. The seduced or raped child often suffers a torn rectum or vagina. Some child-molesters murder their victims after using them for sexual gratification, receiving additional satisfaction from sadistic action. This sadism is also a reversion to an infantile mental stage—that brief period during which a normal child enjoys acts of cruelty such as pulling the cat's tail. In the pervert, this stage is perpetuated. Beyond the physical injury (except murder), the psychological trauma inflicted by the child-molester may well be more damaging and may arrest his victim in an immature stage, producing another pervert.

Such was the case with Mike, who at twenty-three was apprehended after sexually assaulting a twelve-year-old boy on the school grounds. Mike, who was then working as a salesman in a men's shoe store, was a fine-looking but shy young man, who had played football at the high school from which he graduated.

When he was four years old, Mike's widowed mother died, and for the next eight years he lived with his uncle in a bachelor apartment. The uncle, with whom Mike shared bedroom and bed, made the child masturbate him, often rewarding the boy by allowing him to go to a movie. Then, at age twelve, Mike moved to the home of his older sister and her husband, who were religious and straitlaced. For several years his sexual activities were primarily self-masturbation, although at fourteen he did attempt to have intercourse with a neighbor's daughter. With her he was impotent.

Mike became lonely and shy. His favorite recreation was going to movies, especially those with violent action and overly masculine heroes. At home he enjoyed reading and looking at physical culture magazines, which seemed to stimulate him so that he had to relieve himself by masturbation. Apparently he also had several sexual affairs with adult men whom he met at theaters, around magazine stores, and in other such public places.

As a football player in high school, Mike was liked and admired by schoolmates of both sexes. He enjoyed the company of younger admirers and "looked after them," bringing them candy and other gifts whenever he could. When he was eighteen he went with a friend to a prostitute, but could not have satisfactory sex relations with her, explaining that he felt uncomfortable with girls and believed that men were more "natural." Once, when visiting relatives in another city, he met a young man in a movie and paid him to perform fellatio.

During his early twenties, Mike became involved in a robbery and was convicted but received a suspended sentence. When he was subsequently arrested for assaulting a boy, he said that he felt like a "big brother" to the child and "did not mean to harm him." Mike was sorry that the boy had to be hospitalized, but did not feel that he had done anything wrong—except perhaps he should have found "a more co-operative boy." Mike claimed to have a girl friend, who proved to be a fourteen-year-old who performed oral masturbation for him.

This pervert's bashfulness is characteristic of his basic sense of inferiority and his masochism. Because of his early seduction by his uncle, Mike is impotent with female sex partners and feels inadequate with adult male sex partners, with whom his childhood experiences were in a passive role. He prefers children because they inflate his feeling of dominance and desire for power. The pornographic movies and magazines, although not directly related to his early traumatic sexual experience, helped to cement the psychopathic sex structure.

Every adult pervert is the product of premature sexual stimulation in childhood, whether it is due to actual attacks or to overexposure as an observer to sexual activities. Never before in history have children and youngsters been so overwhelmingly and continuously exposed to adult and perverted sexual activity and sadism as they are today through the so-called "entertainment media" of motion pictures, television, and popular literature. The effect on the child's psychosexual structure is comparable to the effect on his bone structure when he is forced to walk too soon.

A child crawls before he walks. He does not naturally or normally try to walk, or even stand erect, until his bones and muscles are sufficiently developed to carry his weight in the upright position. If his parents force him to walk before he is naturally prepared to do so, the child's legs will become permanently bowed. He will suffer from this unsightly deformity throughout his life unless he undergoes lengthy and uncomfortable medical treatment with properly fitted orthopedic braces and perhaps surgery.

The effect of "forced" or premature experiences in a child's sexual development is even more damaging. The child

naturally progresses through various stages of sensual awareness from infancy to adulthood. If he is introduced to mature
sexual experiences before his mental apparatus is ready to
cope with them, he may—like the child who learns to walk
prematurely—develop a certain capacity for such acts, but
it will be at the price of mental distortion or perversion.
This deformity in his psychosexual development may or may
not be able to be corrected by skilled psychiatric treatment.
And unlike bowlegs, sexual deformity harms others as well
as himself.

It is simple enough to understand that the seduction of
a child by an adult is a direct assault on, the child. Yet
parents who shudder at such a thought complacently expose
their children to sexual seduction and sadism day after day
in their own living rooms via the TV screen and permit
them or even escort them to the even more blatant over-
exposure of the motion-picture screen.

Here are the highlights of the bill of fare offered for our
mental and emotional consumption on the movie pages of
a newspaper serving a family area of over seven million people— the *Los Angeles Times*, on an average midweek day,
1970:

Karla—is no lady . . . wicked as can be
The Puppet Women—explains love by rote
Up the Chimney—for those who don't like simulation
Snow Job—for the girl who's tried everything
The Stewardesses—we defend your right to see it
Fanny Hill—from the country that gave you *I, a Woman*
Man and Wife—49 ways of "expressing love."——See it with some-
one you would like to love. Adults over 21—or marriage license.

plus,

*Infrasexum; Sun City, Acapulco Uncensored; The Activist; Me-
dium Cool; The Masterpiece; Over 18 and Ready; Paint Her
Delicious; Frisco Zingers; The Damned; Let There Be Boys;
Place for Lovers; Realities of Female Behavior; Wild Girls;
Male/Female; Best House in London*

What sort of mental fare is this for adults—much less for the young people who fill movie houses? What outraged protests would be heard if we or our children were served tainted meat, spoiled vegetables, polluted water!

The libertines in the entertainment industry have managed, by sheer endurance, to influence practically all movies. G- and GP-rated movies desensitize popcorn-munching children to acts of wantonness.

G-rated movies have come to mean one sex scene; GP, at least two; R, three or more; X, ad lib. For example:

Darling Lili (G)—Promoted in Los Angeles by permitting children accompanied by parents to attend free, it has first a bedroom and then a bathroom sex scene. In the latter, the nude, showering heroine is forcefully confronted by the hero, whom she slaps in the face for calling her a virgin.

They Might Be Giants (G)—The heroine, a psychiatrist, attends a movie with her patient. Sitting in back of them is a young couple engaging in intense lovemaking. Reaching a state of sensual frenzy, the lovers strip off their clothes, clutch each other, and start to have sexual intercourse. When the heroine calls the usher to stop them, he throws her out of the theater for disturbing the regular customers.

The Sicilian Clan (GP)—Shows the entirely nude heroine having an adulterous sex act while her five-year-old nephew watches.

Cheyenne Social Club (GP)—A full-length exhortation to prostitution.

Butch Cassidy and the Sundance Kid (GP)—Disperses scenes of bordello-style sex and a rape in a picture about old-time Western train-robbers.

Flap (GP)—Advertised as a comedy, it dramatizes the toilet habits of Anthony Quinn, the hero, and his frequent visits to prostitutes. The heroine, his choice prostitute, catches Quinn in bed with another harlot and tries to cut off his genital with shears.

The R-rated movies for seventeen-year-olds and older viewers are replete with more vivid displays of the sex act; most include, at least, a modicum of perversion.

The X-rated, for the avant-garde and the not-so-sophisticated adults, emphasize gung-ho orgies.

The restrictive "Adults Only" phrase never appears on TV, books, or magazines. When it is applied occasionally in connection with a motion picture—or when the other media are banned or censored by various monitoring groups—the restriction merely serves to whet youthful appetites for a taste of the forbidden fruit. However, this fruit is dished out so lavishly without restrictions that the apologetic fine-print disclaimer "For Adults Only" has little meaning. If the producers and publishers were really desirous of protecting the public's mental and emotional health, the majority of their products today should be labeled in large type:

WARNING!

This motion picture extols the virtues of perversion and its use may lead to serious sexual maladjustments.

An argument used to defend showing such entertainment is that no one is forced to attend a movie, watch television, or read a book. The argument is not valid. The human mind is compelled to find temporary relief from man's vulnerability in a realistic world. Escape in the fantasy world of stories is as necessary as food. (Archeologists find this need existed even in prehistoric man.) To participate in such outlets is a basic human right. Those responsible for providing the means for these reliefs from tension are not privileged to ignore the normal individual.

Another favorite dictum of pornographers and their defenders is the saying that "no girl was ever ruined by a book." Max Levin, M.D., author of "Psychiatric Notes," printed monthly in the *Current Medical Digest*, says, "I doubt that this view is widely held by psychiatrists—no one can doubt that some youngsters are affected adversely by pornographic and sadistic literature that overflows the paperback shelves— even those youngsters who are not sick to begin with."

Modern youth cannot attend a movie, read a currently

popular book, browse at a magazine stand, or watch television without being flooded with perverse information. Over-exposure to the portrayal of adult sex, sexual perversion, and sadistic violence overwhelms the conscious barrier in immature minds, admitting a flood of dangerous instinctual energies that are unrelated to the present environment. In the grip of these uncontrolled energies, the mind becomes alienated from reality. Unnatural, abnormal behavior results. The Boston Strangler, for example, who terrorized that city by murdering and mutilating middle-aged women, claimed that he had gotten the idea for part of his method of operation from a television program.

The perversion, sadism, and masochism which the entertainment media spews out into our society arrests sexual development in, or causes regression to, the stage of satisfactions from cruelty. No success in this field seems to be without the cruelty message.

No self-respecting hero of the media would treat his love object with respect and warmth. To show emotional displays of affection would make him a "stupid square." To be a man and be appreciated by the heroine, he must beat her in at least one scene. Another scene must depict him as a "real male" by showing him taking a merciless beating without whimpering. Such extremes of sadism and masochism are portrayed as normal. There must also be at least one sex orgy, which relegates the entire development of human sexuality to indulging in the sex act, usually with deviations and perversions. Natural or truly normal sexual development is severely handicapped.

Dr. Lawrence J. Hatterer of Cornell University, in a paper given before the American Academy of Psychoanalysis, concluded that homosexuality could be triggered by environmental stimuli. Among the most important triggers, Dr. Hatterer said, are suggestive homosexual literature, plays, and movies.

Dr. Nicholas G. Frignito, Medical Director and Chief

Psychiatrist of the County Court of Philadelphia, points out:
"The most singular factor inducing the adolescent to sexual
activities is pornography. . . . The increase in sexual offenses
among adults, too, is directly attributed to pornography."

It is virtually impossible for the inexperienced, youthful
mind to evaluate properly the portrayals in the mass media,
which are usually in direct contrast to the ideals taught by
parents.

Obscenity and Pornography

XXIX

~~~~~~

What Price Sex Education?

MELVIN ANCHELL, M.D., ABFP
11633 San Vicente Boulevard, Suite 320
Los Angeles, California 90049

Morton A. Hill, S.J.
Morality in Media, Inc.
487 Park Avenue
New York, New York 10022

Dear Reverend Hill:

In response to your request for information regarding current
sex courses, I am enclosing a copy of my talk, *What Price Sex
Education?* This material was first given to a school district in
Minneapolis where the PTA Council invited me to present my
viewpoints.
Best regards.

Sincerely,
Melvin Anchell, M.D., ABFP

On May 13, 1970, leading sex education proponents were
invited to appear in Washington before the Presidential Commission on Obscenity and Pornography. The educators' mission was to convince the Commission that sex education, as
currently advocated by such groups as SIECUS, was a means
of counteracting the effects of pornography on young people. The mission was accomplished.

In its report to the nation, the Commission's majority members recommended adoption of libertine school sex programs to offset pornography. Curiously, in the same report, they concluded that pornography played no role in the causation of social or individual harm.

As a result of testifying as an expert witness in court cases concerning sex education and pornography, I have had opportunity to examine much of these materials. In the light of psychological knowledge and direct medical experience, the assumptions of the current new breed of educators and the Commission are horrendously and inexcusably fallacious. One can only conclude that their propaganda serves as a monument to sexual ignorance, or else that it is one of the greatest frauds ever perpetrated on American society. Why these people are determined to sell debased sexuality to the public is beyond ordinary comprehension.

For references, the sex experts rely on the academic works of sex professors such as Masters and Johnson and of sex advisors such as the Presidential Commission on Obscenity and Pornography. However, truth concerning sex cannot be pried loose by means of test-tube experiments and questionnaires. Professors in institutions are far removed from the realities of everyday life. So are the findings emanating from ivory-towered college laboratories patterned after bordellos. In the "Masters and Johnson School," scholars take notes and motion pictures while watching through peepholes the sexual antics of paid and unpaid volunteers. Some of their performers are sent to motels and hotels to engage in sex acts. Afterward they are debriefed by the enthusiastic sex professors.

The Pornography Commission, taking its cue from the college investigators, conducted its own experiments. Providing subjects with an ample supply of erotic material and cups, the Commission endeavored to determine the effects of pornography by measuring the amount of semen ejaculated into the receptacles. With all due respect for their sexually abused subjects, the Commission might just as well have used gorillas or chimpanzees. Sexually mature persons could not have participated in such investigations. They would become impotent under the circumstances.

Psychoanalysis demands long and intense attention to the individual patient. It is wasteful to squander time and money on such inane experiments; and, I feel, a crime for men in affluent positions to foster sexual nonsense upon the public.

The sex academicians purposely avoided actual life situations. The Commission "wouldn't be caught dead" in local pornographic establishments because, it said, pornographic standards varied between communities. Bypassing pornography as it exists in reality was most inappropriate. In one of my communications with the Commission, I suggested they make a more critical analysis by examining real down-to-earth situations, rather than eroticized cup-holders. I offered to provide an hour and a half taped interview with one of my Los Angeles patients, a 21-year-old college student who is a locally acclaimed topless-bottomless dancer. Her firsthand, unbiased account of the effects of topless-bottomless dancing on night club patrons, I felt, would help the Commission reevaluate its conclusion that pornography and obscenity cause no harm. However, the Commission felt it could not depend on the observations of clinicians daily involved with the effects of debased sexuality on patients. The Commission seemed desirous of ignoring anything that might show obscenity and pornography did cause social and individual harm.

It is unfortunate that the sex advisors to this nation disregard the most elementary psychology regarding human sexuality. They appear to lack an understanding of the nature of civilization and its relationship to sexual behavior. The majority of the Presidential Commission and SIECUS-oriented educators are unknown to me personally. I have no private desire for dissension with them. However, because of the fearful damage their advice will cause society, I have written

this paper. Hopefully, the psychological facts will act as an
antidote.

I.

My criterion for opposing the present type of sex educators
and the Commission's findings is not based upon concepts of
"right" or "wrong." The standard used for judging their
works depends only on what is "correct" or "incorrect." As a
physician, I consider anything that supports life and helps man
live until he succumbs from natural causes as *correct*. Anything that destroys life or prematurely causes death is *incorrect*.

The character and intellectual refinement of civilized communities inextricably depend upon curtailing basic instincts.
Only by placing restrictions on the raw instinctual energies
inherited by every individual at birth have cultured societies
been able to emerge from earlier primitive horde groups.
Modulation of instincts is accomplished by reinforcing mental
controls—conscience and ego—with social inhibitions—family
and religion.

The sexual instinct is most highly developed in man. Even
the most primitive societies do not tolerate a direct expression
of sex. For survival, they have many customs and taboos
associated with sexuality and the manner in which sexual desires are vented. By controlling direct sexual energies and
partially converting them to other uses, civilizations have
evolved.

Freud's statement in *Sex and the Psychology of Love* suc-
cinctly describes the development of civilization:

> Our civilization is founded on the suppression of instincts.
> From these sources the common stock of the material and
> ideal wealth of civilization has been accumulated. . . . Human
> civilization rests upon two pillars, one of which is the re-
> striction of our instincts and the other the control of natural
> forces. As regards the sexual instincts, in most people they

are tamed insufficiently and in a manner which is psychologically wrong and are therefore readier than the rest to break loose.

The sexual instinct is probably more strongly developed in man than most of the higher animals. It places an extraordinary amount of energy at the disposal of cultural activities. ... The ability to exchange originally sexual aims for others which are no longer sexual *is called the capacity for sublimation.*

Concerning the role of family and religion in civilization, he says,

Over and above the struggle for existence, it is chiefly family feeling which has induced the individuals to make this renunciation of sexual and aggressive tendencies. This renunciation has been a progressive one in the evolution of civilization. ... The steps in it were sanctioned by religion.

A free, democratic society is mankind's highest social achievement. Individuals living in such societies are independent and self-governing. Use of their critical faculties and self-responsibilities are stressed. They elect or vote out leaders, who are critically watched while in office.

In less advanced societies, or when a civilization regresses, independence and initiative are lost. Consciences disappear among the members and personal interests are sacrificed to collective interest. Dissimilarities between individuals are removed and an average character comes through. The society takes on the characteristics of a horde. Members are held together by a dictatorial authority. Self-government is replaced by obedience to and unquestioning faith in the leader. Individuals become more barbarian, that is, creatures acting by instinct and requiring immediate fulfillment of all their needs.

2.

Today's youths are encouraged to renounce the mental and social restraints over their instinctual energies. This causes re

gression to more primitive stages of life. The Pied Pipers
leading young people in this direction consist largely of ultra-
libertine avant garde leaders (including some politicians, educators and theologians) who champion pornography in the
mass media and in schools.

The sex-pushers influence youths to ignore laws and
family values and to set up new values based on "doing
your own thing." For strength, the indoctrinated young people band together, forming unstructured groups which resist
any impediments to the straightforward fulfillment of physical desires—especially sex. Leaders capable of complete control over other members spring up in the groups. The leader's
goals become those of the group. His orders are followed
without question. The members' loyalties to the leader are
responsible for their unwavering allegiance to each other.
These are the characteristics found in horde cultures.

A chief source adding to the retrogression of American culture is the motion-picture industry. A constant stream of
motion pictures, catering to adolescents and young adults,
gushes forth, glorifying primitive ways of life and associated
sexual behaviors. Identification with degenerate heroes and
heroines in movies such as *Easy Rider* establish the ideal for
immature egos.

Aside from the commercial media and others gutting society, the most unkind cut of all comes from the new breed
of sex educators. The Pied Pipers of the schools are leading
exponents for bringing down the time-tested virtues of the
Judeo-Christian morality, which they claim to protect.
Throughout the current "family life—sex education programs" there is a conscious and substantial undermining which
discredits family and religion. Students are taught to rely
entirely on their own inexperienced and immature judgments
and those of their peers. As traditional morality is damned by
faint praise, sexual openness is intensified.

The sex material used in schools is essentially the same
found in commercial pornography. However, the pornog-

raphy presented in schools is more damaging to the child. Students suspect that debased sexuality in movies, magazines, and books is make-believe; but similar presentations given by teachers are regarded as truth.

3.

Some educators have a compulsion to teach sex beginning with the three-year-old continuing until high school graduation. Uninterrupted information would be given about genital anatomy, masturbation, coitus (in animals and humans), venereal disease, contraception, obstetrical techniques, and perversion. The educators proclaim that in this way children will be taught healthy sexual adjustments. VD and illegitimate pregnancies will be controlled and the adverse effects of pornography will be nullified.

Originally, parents were assured that the courses would consider the moral aspects of sex. Now, however, after having become firmly entrenched in the school systems, the sex teachers claim they have been put upon—that moral education is not their responsibility but that of family and church.

Children indoctrinated by such sex educators have no wordly chance of making mature sexual adjustments. Perversion and impotence are their lot. The students and the civilization of which they are a part are destroyed.

4.

Psychoanalysis has established that the period in a child's life between ages of six and twelve is asexual, during which sensual pleasures are normally suppressed. This repression is an inborn mental process and unrelated to social restraints. It exists in primitive as well as civilized people. The period is well recognized by psychiatrists throughout the world and has been designated as the "latency period."

During latency the first stirring of compassionate feelings

arises in the human mind. Compassion develops when sexual energies are converted into affection. The affectionate love in the asexual stage of childhood is felt for parents, or those responsible for the child's total care. Later in life, this love is also felt for other love objects.

Compassion for one's fellowman is a relatively new instinct —a need recently created to aid human survival. It marks a notable step forward in removing civilized man from the savage. Compassion has not had much time to become securely developed. Only a few centuries separate our civilization from that which fed humans to lions as sport. This new and valuable instinct is dangerously attacked by surreptitiously devaluating the family life of preteen youths and sexually overstimulating them. Such interferences prevent affectionate development. The results can be increasingly noted in the antisocial behavior of pseudo independent, sexually over-stuffed schoolchildren.

Preventing the conversion of sexual impulses into compassion is not the only problem brought on by sex educators who meddle with the latency period. The suppression of sexual energies in the 6- to 12-year-old is also responsible for a desire to learn. Sexual curiosity is converted into curiosity for knowledge in general. When the child at this age is made prematurely wise sexually, his normal mental or psychological growth is stunted. He grows up with a hunger for a society that will continue to take care of him as a parent would rather than with a thirst for creative independence.

In natural development, preteen children derive sexual pleasure from sensualized excitements caused by sexual fantasies. Sex educators who catapult the child into a world of authoritative sexual knowledge shatter these normal satisfactions. The resultant frustrations tend to fix the child in these early stages of sexual growth. Later in life, drugs and pornography are used as adjuncts to help recapture the pleasures from unresolved and unforgotten childhood fantasies.

By means of denial or social blackmail, sex educators evade any psychological or social facts standing in their way. Regarding the latency period, they either refuse to admit it exists, or claim that it is due to hang-ups in the child. Parents who object to K-12 courses are accused of neglecting their children because of sexual embarrassment or ignorance. The educators threaten to take matters into their own hands, should the parents fail to cooperate. Using these Mafia tactics and the Hitlerian doctrine that if a lie is told often enough and forcefully enough people will believe it, educational quackery is forced onto the public.

5.

Sex is an intimate affair. Two people in love seek solitude during sexual relations. They guard each other from infringements of voyeurists, exhibitionists, free-lovers, and pornography. Though they are willing to share affectionate feelings with family and mankind in general, they are intolerant about sharing sexual love with others. The intrusions of outsiders cause intense feelings of shame and jealousy, and make normal people impotent for performing sex openly or with a group.

Exhibitionism and voyeurism presented in razzle-dazzle sex classes tend to cause undue interest in the childhood stage of sexual development where nudity is the primary sexual excitation. The truth is that young people should be taught modesty regarding nudity to prevent their becoming fixed in, or regressing to, this five-year-old sexual stage. In mature individuals, nudity is ancillary, not primary to the genital sex act.

Feeling shame at public displays of pornography and showing embarrassment at intrusions made in one's private sex life are natural reactions. Coeducational sex classes desensitize boys and girls to public expressions of sex and encourage them to engage in intimacies openly. Promiscuity, impotence, and perversions are the scholastic achievements.

Proper sexual growth should develop character. Studies of the mind show that character, like compassion, is formed by suppression of some sexual urges—especially masturbation. In normal family life, parents help build character by discouraging masturbation for frequent orgasms. Current sex courses condone masturbation and teach various techniques for achieving orgasms through self-excitations.

A few years ago, anyone debating sex educators could prove his contentions simply by presenting the material taught. As that time, the educators were sensitive about this matter. They tried to conceal it. Now they readily admit the material used, point an accusing finger, and cry "sexual hang-up" at anyone opposing their classroom pornography.

Recently, a chief sex professor told me he failed to sell his textbook to the leading California school district promoting sex instruction because the book was not "raw enough." The sexperts proclaim that in the new mainstream of contemporary life, "chastity and mature sex are out—free love and perversion are in."

The sexual instinct, however, cannot be altered by the proclamations of man-made "sexual revolutions."

Normal sex requires tender feelings and affectionate esteem for one's love object. To reiterate, individuals can fall in love or be in love only when they learn to convert physical sex aims into compassion. The greater the sublimation, the more profound is devotion for the loved person. Only when affectionate bonds are firmly established—a condition that ordinarily necessitates marriage—can affectionate and sexual feelings become readily interchangeable.

By their loyalty, normal parents teach children that sex is a one woman—one man affair. The sex educator's advice, "sex is for fun," desecrates the affectionate and monogamous nature of human sexuality.

A debased environment can transform affectionate love

between two people into feelings having direct physical aims only. The destruction of the mental sexual component is a prime cause for today's increased adultery, divorce, perversion, antisocial behavior, and fewer marriages.

Pornographically and sexually saturated youths and adults, whom I see in my office and in much of the Los Angeles community, seem beset with anxiety and unhappiness. Clinical findings verify Freud's statement that

> an investigation of cases of common nervousness has led me to the conclusion that these disorders could be traced to contemporary abuses in the patient's sexual life and could be removed if these were brought to an end.

Though environmental abuses in Freud's time were due to *overly suppressing mature sexual relations,* the abuses in our time result *from condoning free love and perversion.* The results of the sexual wrongs in these two eras may be measured by the amount of perversion, suicide, pornography, obscenity, divorce, moral laxity, drug abuse, criminality, and antisocial behavior that existed in the early 1900s and the early 1970s.*

6.

A type of case that seems most pathetic to me, and one I see with increasing frequency, is that of the virginal adolescent girl who, indoctrinated by sex education and desensitized to modesty and sexual intimacy, learns to believe that extramarital sex is proper. Though she is uncritical of others engaging in sex acts, she says, she avoids becoming involved because she

---

* It may be of interest to note here that after the Russian Revolution, Russian leaders became intolerant of free love, pornography, and perversion. In Russia today, marriage and family are highly esteemed and idolized. Nothing is allowed to jeopardize these institutions. Sex education, the type our sex educators have in mind, is not permitted. By contrast Communists and radical New Left leaders in the Western world invariably support free love, pornography, sex education, and the removal of all statutes controlling perversion. This technique is cynically used as propaganda to "divide and conquer."

has no need. Her sexual fantasies usually resemble the experiences of sexy heroines in today's movies and books. She identifies with these females and believes they represent sexually adjusted women.

When this young girl falls in love she is easily persuaded to have intercourse. She has been led to believe the sex act will enhance love. However, the boy's love for her, devoid of profound affectionate ties, is rapidly dissipated by the sex act. Before affectionate or sexual needs for her can build up again, he usually finds another sexually prone partner and abandons the first girl.

The young girl rarely, if ever, experiences any real satisfaction, much less orgasm, during intercourse. Her need after "giving herself" is to be reassured she is loved. Not understanding her abandonment, she develops feelings of inferiority. An inner bitterness comes about toward males, who she feels are generally insincere. Subconsciously, she suspects her lover left because she proved lacking in femininity or because her sexual organs were inadequate. For guidance and reassurance she turns to other females who appear sexually satisfied. Most frequently, her "satisfied" friends have experienced her same disappointments, which they try to conceal with promiscuity. Continued experimentation, they hope, will make them femmes fatales and teach them how to enslave the male with sexual enrapturement. To hide guilt feelings and frustrations, some females bottle up sexual energies and use them for "cause célèbres." The glorified heroine in the pornographic movie *I Am Curious (Yellow)** represents an example of such psychosexual adjustments. Empathetic American viewers are led to believe that the heroine depicts the sexual behavior of a normal girl in a permissive environment. While going about belittling socioeconomic systems opposed to Communist philosophies, she is shown engaging in frequent acts of genital, oral, and anal intercourse. This movie was filmed in Sweden

* Found obscene by the courts in Phoenix, Arizona, where I testified as one of the prosecutor's expert witnesses.

where pornography laws have been repealed and statutes controlling perversion removed.

7.

The sexual instinct has two physical aims—the need for sensual pleasure and the need for propagation. Bear in mind, however, that the genital sex act is not necessarily a mature one. When students test out what is learned in school, the boy simply masturbates intravaginally and the girl acts as a pill-protected receptacle for sperm. Children robbed of normal sexual growth cannot fulfill the physical—much less mental—aims of the sexual instinct.

Sexually stunted patients I have analyzed, whose early sex experiences resemble those of mechanical robots, frequently resort to drugs and perversions to overcome impotence. Others may compensate by suppressing all sexual activities and use their libidinal energies for social, cultural, or scholarly pursuits. Some become fanatic advocators of weird philosophical groups to keep from returning to their more sexually debased, nightmarish lives.

8.

"Freedom now," and "I've got to be free" are common slogans in today's society. Freedom is a noble word, but in a free society it requires that an individual consider the needs of others when satisfying his own. For horde cultures, freedom means "doing one's own thing" irrespective of others. Sex, hate, and other primary urges are expressed without restraint.

In the name of freedom, today's sex educators encourage students to "go overboard" in tolerance for perversion. The first natural reaction of the normal person toward perverts is to shun the abnormal, as a subconscious protective defense against contamination. When disgust turns to sympathy, the normal individual becomes defenseless. When the natural sex-

ual instincts become perverted, the death instinct takes over.
The frustrations of perverts and free-lovers drive them to
self-destruction. Some destroy themselves rapidly by suicide;
others succumb more slowly with drugs, alcohol, or disease.
In addition, intended love objects are harmed by the perverts'
sadisms.

Perverts and their avant garde sophist supporters proclaim
that sensual pleasures derived from infantile stages of self-
love are achievements over mature sexual relations. They
look upon normal people as uneducated "squares." Deviates
not infrequently attain affluent positions from which they re-
cruit others. Even the mature adult may be influenced by
the sophists' intellectualisms. The growing army of free-lovers
and perverts extol the virtues they find by engaging openly
in sex with partners having equal value and serving only for
the purpose of orgasm. These practices were prevalent in prehistoric times when "being in love" played no part in human
sexuality. Adults are desensitized to accept free love and
hippie communal sex by pornography. Children are desensitized to accept group sex practices and perversion by sex
education.

9.

For support, today's sex educators, the Pornography Commission, and sex professors turn to social workers, psycholo-
gists, and psychiatrists who agree that obscenity and pornography are harmless. The champions of debased sex simply
ignore the vast number of concerned professionals in these
fields who do not agree.

The majority opinion of any organization is frequently a
reflection of social pressures and the pet theories of persuasive
leaders. In medicine, especially, this situation holds true.
Throughout history, physicians have bent to the view of
those in control.

The American professors' whitewash of pornography is

declaimed by colleagues in other countries throughout the world.

A few years ago, leading professionals from 85 countries and the United States met at the United Nations to consider the effects of the mass media on antisocial behavior. The foreign delegates expressed shocked disbelief at the U.S. delegates' disavowal of the media's harmful effects. According to Dr. Lejuns, Professor of Sociology, University of Maryland, who attended the meeting, the foreign representatives had the impression that the American attitude was due to his country's greed for making money by appealing to the baser elements of human nature.

An audit of the profits accruing to the suppliers and promoters of the new pornography—in the guise of "sex education"—might well prove that the foreign observers were right.

Far greater than the money involved, however, is the price we are paying in human destruction. When the slowly evolved compassionate and affectionate components of human sexuality are completely devalued, and sex debased to mere physical gratification, the human being and his society are catapulted back into the abyss from which man so laboriously climbed for a hundred thousand years.

XXX

~~~~~~

A Work of Art

Art (ärt), n.1. The quality, production, expression, or realm of what is beautiful.

—*Random House College Dictionary*

Schickel's Masterpiece

In the late 1960s, a movie, *Closely Watched Trains*, was produced in Czechoslovakia. The movie was forbidden in that country as well as in other Eastern nations. It was highly touted and widely distributed, however, throughout the Western world. Leading American reviewers proclaimed it a landmark in cinematic history.

The review of *Closely Watched Trains* written by the notable Richard Schickel was printed in *Life* magazine and treated with preeminence. Mr. Schickel enthusiastically bestowed one accolade after another on the film's merits. *Closely Watched Trains*, he said,

. . . has an excellent chance of becoming a film classic on the order of Grand Illusion or Citizen Kane.

. . . one of those pictures that is never out of release.

. . . will continue to inform the sensibilities of generations yet to come.

. . the best movie I have ever seen.

After reading the review, my wife and I were eager to see the movie. In a theater filled to capacity with adolescents on dates, we were immediately immersed by the movie into a bouillabaisse of unvarnished sexual degeneracy· Vividly portrayed on the screen were scenes of: (1) Impotence—the story concerns an anguished, sexually impotent seventeen-year-old menial worker for the village railroad station; (2) Incest—the impotent youth leaves his sexually frustrated sweetheart lying in her uncle's bed where she waits for the older man to satisfy her; (3) Masochism—as the camera focuses on the disappointed hero immersed in a bathtub, his unclothed body is gradually obliterated by the crimson blood gushing from his slashed wrists; (4) Masturbation—recovering from his attempted suicide, the youth seeks sexual advice from the old village woman. Grasping a goose held firmly in her groin, she gazes fixedly with a sensual grin as she unfeignedly masturbates the goose's stiffened neck; (5) Adultery—the lecherousness of the stationmaster alienates him from his wife; (6) Bestiality—the stationmaster breaks into salacious sweats whenever he compares the village matron's buttocks with those of her horse; (7) Lewdness—the dispatcher, a shrewd womanizer, keeps the station's waiting room sofa in constant need of repair due to the violence of his frequent sex acts with young women; (8) Exhibitionism—in a state of sexual frenzy, the dispatcher uses railway markers to stamp the buttocks of the unclothed girl lying prone on the letter-sorting table; (9) Orgies—the come-hither coyness of the nurses, quartered in a railroad car outside the station, inflames the wantonness of visiting Nazi soldiers; (10) Sadism—the sadistic sex killer is tried by the village court for strangling one of his hapless partners; (11) Free love—learning of the young hero's impotence, an attractive underground freedom fighter—and free lover—is overcome with motherliness. Clutching the lad to her bosom, she coaxes him onto the dispatcher's broken-down couch. With motherly caresses admixed with adroit sexual

talents, she manages to get him to perform the sex act for her;
(12) Suicide—overjoyed with the accomplishment, the youth
loses his depression and develops a mania to display manliness.
As a "closely watched" Nazi ammunition train passes the
station, he jumps aboard and sets off explosions. The final
scene shows fragmented bits and pieces of the blown-up train
and hero raining over the countryside. To the blaring sounds
of military music heard above the dynamite explosions, the
curtain falls.

In his review, Schickel made several predictions that have
come true. *Closely Watched Trains* will continue "to inform
the sensibilities of generations yet to come," he said. Indeed,
the picture conventionalized sexual indecency in motion pictures. It acted as a spearhead openng the doors of everyday
theaters to subjects which were previously limited to skid
row. This "classic film" was followed by a flood of sexploita-
tion movies produced by an industry catering to eighteen- to
twenty-four-year-old patrons.

More recently, the shows *Hair, I Am Curious (Yellow)*,
Oh! Calcutta!, and *Without a Stitch* have been produced and
acclaimed by some critics. Apparently, these new spearheads
will be used as models for future pornography.

During World War II, this country endured the persistent
threats and offenses of its enemies until Pearl Harbor made
the dangers unbearable. Hopefully, movie obscenities of the
early 1970s will fail to serve as fresh spearheads, but will act,
instead, as a Pearl Harbor, arousing the nation to the fact that
pornographers are gutting the very entrails from America's
moral life.

"Attaboy, Attaboy, Attaboy"

The sensibilities of moviegoers, young and old, are strongly
affected by the judgments of movie reviewers. Show business, too, relies on the sophisticated perceptions of these
connoisseurs to determine what is "a work of art."

Obscene movies find little, if any, opposition from many of today's critics. On the contrary, reviewers ofttimes provide prime support for cinematic vulgarities. Reviews appearing in weekly magazines reflect the attitude of nationally prominent reviewers toward debauchery in the cinema. From among the numerous film releases, the November 17, 1970, issue of *Newsweek* selected three movies, *The Owl and the Pussycat*, *Groupies*, and *Ice*, for review.

The Owl and the Pussycat:
With *The Owl and the Pussycat* we can resume the enjoyment of the real Barbra Streisand. . . . Now all the circus junk and the mastodon droppings have been cleared away and we have Streisand plain. There she comes . . . white boots scrambling, tote bag swinging, cursing out a departing bus. . . .

In *The Owl and the Pussycat* Streisand is your friendly neighborhood hooker, the streets made flesh . . . no love, no nothing but her TV set. . . . The other half of the couple is George Segal as Felix. . . . They live in the same New York hotel . . . and the upshot is a hilarious quasi-copulation. . . .

Later on they remove the quasi in a funky love scene from which one will never be able to forget Streisand's lovely spinal furrow and her frenetically healthy urgency as she scrambles in the sheets, coaxing the nonprofessional Segal breathlessly with "Attaboy, attaboy, attaboy." Afterward they start the inevitable backlash, she using a paperback vocabulary-builder to put him down, he ranting at her vulgarity: "I may be a prostitute," she says, "but I'm not promiscuous."

The movie's basic device is indeed vulgarity—Streisand's two-word obscenity is going to be a landmark movie expostulation. The surprising merit of the film, is how much mileage it gets out of its vulgarity—director Herbert Ross gives us a New York of how it really is. The streets are lined with streetwalkers and the movie houses are bordellos with popcorn stands. A fellow stops at the corner newsstand and the newslady holds a paper up to his nose and asks "Screw?" In Central Park, dogs are humping each other.

America's number one box-office attraction, Barbra Streisand, fornicating on the screen with George Segal, is applauded by the reviewer. He also feels that Miss Streisand's rendition of "Attaboy, attaboy, attaboy" will henceforth give these words sensual meaning.

The reviewer's appreciation of these sex scenes causes me to think of John C's case. John C is a twenty-six-year-old patient who teaches sex education in an indigent section of Los Angeles. His wife, a thirty-three-year-old divorcée, has normal sexual desires and encourages John to have marital relationships. However, because of psychosexual experiences in early life, John prefers to take his wife to R or X movies and, after returning home, to masturbate while he recounts the sex scenes to her. An exhibitionist-voyeurist, Mr. C prefers orgasms resulting from seeing and showing rather than from marital intercourse.

The reviewer regards showing Central Park dogs united in sexual union as a cinema achievement, for, he suggests, "it tells it like it is." Cultural standards have not sunk to this level, however. Dramatizations of human fornication and bestial sex habits are still considered obscene. Incessant bombardment with show-business indecencies eventually may cause a decay in this nation's artistic values; but until that eventuality, *Newsweek's* educated reviewer must know that his highly praised sex scenes are uncouth. Surely he must have known, too, that analytically, his manifest reason for appreciating bestiality would be considered suspect. Longingly, the adulatory review is concluded with

At the end . . . through the humping of dogs, they [Streisand and Segal] depart—simple sensual people.

Many enthusiasts for movie exhibitionism appear also to be devotees of motion pictures that advocate replacing culture with degeneracy and overthrowing command of the government by radical renegades.

Excerpts from *Newsweek*'s reviews of *Groupies* and *Ice* provide these comments:

Groupies:
... is a chatty, color documentary ... offers a glimpse of some of the girls who traded in their bodies for a little glitter. ... Patty Cakes, one of *Groupies*' sexually unabashed rock mascots says, "You get to ball the prettiest boys, smoke the best dope, meet all the most far-out people."
If you're interested ... *Groupies* is your cup of grass. ...
... They [*Groupies*' people] have an undeniable insouciant charm. ...
... The musical numbers underscore the sexuality of rock. ...

Ice:
Robert Kramer, a director who is also a leftist radical, knows and, in a most intimate way, says something about people committed to overthrowing the system. He says it in *Ice*. ...
... In *Ice*, the reasons for revolution are no longer an issue; the time for meaningful dialogue has passed. ...
... As one girl tells it (there are no actors in *Ice*, only familiar-looking city people), she no longer wants to be punished for her rebellion, or to be caught. If she dies, she knows her friends will come to her funeral and someday "avenge" her.
These are not in themselves either chilling or affecting sentiments. In *Ice* they exist as simply stated reality.
The film traces the activities of a group of New York City guerrillas at a time when the United States is engaged in a war of aggression in Mexico while suppressing freedom at home—Kramer's vision of the not-too-distant future. Curfews are imposed, a shadowy security police hunts down and tortures subversives. Much of *Ice* deals with plans for a "regional offensive"—the occupation of a middle-income housing development and the herding together of residents at gunpoint for political discussion, a sniper assassination, the liberation of prisoners and the murder of an informer.
Kramer is less concerned with these actions and more with how these people adapt to their revolutionary tasks.
At another time we see a young man who, in his anxiety over

what might happen to him if he is caught, cannot perform sexually. One guerrilla shoots up heroin. Other scenes show aspects of domesticity. The quality of life is partly standard counterculture, partly the result of revolutionary commitment, but taken all together it reveals a kind of humanism that Kramer plays off against a dreary, dehumanized city.

Quietly, almost sadly, with perturbing power, the film goes beyond ideology; it does not "attack," propagandize or ask sympathy for the cause. Kramer merely shows that these people, whether they destroy or are destroyed, are at this moment indelibly alive.

One thing is indelibly certain, the sexual behavior and societal life presented in these nationally publicized movies is propaganda that diverges from the means of maintaining our civilization, much less achieving a better one.

Before an adjustment can be made and the damage done can begin to heal, the gangrenous material filling the minds of our society, as the result of much of the commercial entertainment, must stop forming. A cure cannot be hoped for as long as these sources, which depict adult behavior as normally corrupt and perverted, continue to spew forth their venom into the minds of our forthcoming generations.

The Code of the West—Hollywood, U.S.A.

In October, 1968, Senate Bill #372, providing for legal classification of motion pictures, was gaining support in the California Legislature. Before the bill could be properly developed, it was given the "coup de grâce" by bitterly opposed movie people. To avoid legislative control, Mr. Jack Valenti, president of the Motion Picture Association, announced plans for a system of movie classification by the industry itself. The industry declared that self-regulation would provide the same controls as legal regulation. It insisted that legal ratings enforced by law was censorship, but self-ratings determined by industry "experts" and voluntarily enforced was a public service. Assuming the intentions of the Motion Picture Association were sincere, the self-regulation idea was, nevertheless, entirely unworkable. Self-policing provided for no penalties or controls over exhibitors who ignored the recommendations of the "experts." Nor was any legal authority permitted to enforce the code. Theater owners were free to reject the audience restrictions without real sanctions. The Motion Picture Association insisted it did not want to promote obscenity; at the same time, it insisted it would not tolerate any punishments imposed for promoting obscenity.

The rating system has become a sham, a part of show business. Youths' wish to be grown-up is spurred on by the restriction notices. They find little difficulty in seeing off-limit movies. There is no doubt in the movie industry that if a picture enticing young people is given an unfavorable rating, the "experts" can be pressured to change the rating. Nor is there doubt that if a restricted picture entices young people to the box office, the exhibitors will fall over themselves to get and show the movie. Irrespective of code ratings, the determining factor for film distributors is gross. If a picture grosses, it's good; if not, it's bad.

For a movie code to be effective, controls must be provided. Human motivations, which consider self-interests above all else, must be modulated at times by legal means. Theaters should be licensed and their licenses revoked if they break the law. I believe that a code can be enforced only in this way.

The Hollywood code, with its self-appointed rating experts, has created a false sense of security in the public mind, causing an indifferent callousness toward commercial lewdness.

The courts have a right and an obligation to protect the public from the apathy of show business to the encroachment of pornographers.

XXXI

~~~~~~~~~~~~~~~~~~~~~~~~~~~~~~~~~~~~~

Wild Scholasticisms

Notwithstanding the vigorous opposition of the American Civil Liberties Union, Public Law 90–100 was passed, creating the Commission on Obscenity and Pornography. The commission was established in response to Congress's concern about the traffic in obscenity and pornography.

In January, 1968, President Lyndon B. Johnson appointed eighteen members and William B. Lockhart, Dean of the Law School of the University of Minnesota, was named Chairman. Dean Lockhart said that he would refuse to serve unless Mr. Paul Bender, a member of the American Civil Liberties Union, was appointed to the staff. Mr. Bender was made Chief Legal Counsel for the commission.

In June 1969, one of President Johnson's appointees resigned and President Nixon appointed Charles H. Keating, Jr., as his lone representative to the commission. During the two-year life of the commission it met twenty-four times and spent approximately $2,000,000. The commission relied on a staff for its investigations. This staff, according to Charles Keating, Jr., was "basically hired by the Commission Chairman and consisted of persons of mediocre talent, hangers-on in government, or individuals not yet settled on a course in life who accept interim work as a place to light." From the staff findings, the commission prepared a final report. It recommended that Congress use the "Danish solution" for solving the problem of pornography—that is, to remove controls and to repeal laws governing pornography.

When Congress passed Public Law 90–100, creating the commission, it recognized that our nation was reaching a dangerous stage of "sexual shock" from obscenity and pornography. In hospitals set up to give treatment for shock due to injuries, a team of doctors race to save the dying patient's life by struggling to check bleeding, reverse the drop in blood pressure, and provide oxygen. The social surgeons on the Pornography Commission, called in to relieve the national psychological shock from obscenities, used their sociological scalpels to open the wounds from sexual debasements more widely, providing a freer flow of pornography.

The exchange of letters presented in this chapter concern the Report of the Presidential Commission on Obscenity and Pornography.

MELVIN ANCHELL, M.D.
11633 San Vicente Boulevard, Suite 320
Los Angeles, California 90049

October 14, 1970

Hon. Robert N. C. Nix
United States House of Representatives
Subcommittee on Postal Operations
Washington, D. C. 20515

Dear Congressman Nix:

Thank you for your letter of October 9th. Your interest in my testifying before your hearings on the Presidential Commission on Obscenity and Pornography's Report is most complimentary.

For some time I have been in the midst of the battle against those who would make pornography a way of life. The time required away from my medical practice for this singularly important societal matter has been costly; personal efforts to help contain the ever-increasing affluence and power of the opposition have been difficult. However, these private concerns become unimportant where our nation's welfare is concerned.

Enclosed is my critique, "The Psychological Aspects of the Commission on Obscenity and Pornography's Report." It was originally prepared at the request of Mr. Charles H. Keating, Jr.
It will be a privilege to appear before your Committee. Kindly let me know what arrangements you want me to make for my coming to Washington.

Most sincerely,
Melvin Anchell, M.D., ABFP

cc: Thomas R. Kennedy
    Subcommittee Counsel

MELVIN ANCHELL, M.D., ABFP
11633 San Vicente Boulevard, Suite 320
Los Angeles, California 90049

October 1970

Charles H. Keating, Jr.
Commissioner, Presidential
Commission on Obscenity and Pornography
1016 16th Street NW
Washington, D.C. 20036

Dear Mr. Keating:

As you have requested, I am writing this critique concerning the majority members' Effects Report. Enclosed also are my published articles pertaining to the subject. I trust the information will be of value in your preparation of the Minority Report.
The articles contain much of the material I wish to present. However, I am enumerating a few of the salient psychological facts pertinent to the Effects Report.

1.

Human sexuality has been amply studied and discussed by eminent analysts such as Freud, Helene Deutsche, Menninger,

Reik, and others. The correctness of their findings has been un-
equivocally verified clinically. Freud's genius for understanding
the human mind is comparable to Einstein's genius for understanding physical nature. No rational scientist investigating the subject of
relativity would totally ignore Einstein's concepts. Paradoxically,
the commission in its investigations of sexuality chose to ignore
Freudian knowledge. Instead, the majority members relied almost
entirely on the scholastic studies of its staff.

2.

Civilized societies make great demands on the individual's behavior. When these demands are weakened, the mind cannot
cope with base desires and they break forth. The resultant un-
modulated behavior is psychopathic in that it satisfies primary
urges without regard to others. This type of behavior can be
seen in some primitive societies that permit open debaucheries.

Even civilized societies, at times, remove defenses against trans-
gressions. During these periods of bacchanal carnivals, subconscious urges are allowed to come forth unrestrainedly. Aside from
the temporary character of these fantasy interludes, society
realizes they are incorrect for real life. Pornography advocates,
on the other hand, propose that these interludes are permanently
worthwhile.

Knowledgeable authorities who suggest removing controls over
pornography and perversion must be aware that to do so necessitates the dissolution of family and religion.

3.

Mature sexuality fulfills the two purposes of the sexual instinct: it can satisfy reproduction as well as give pleasure. In
patients whose sexuality has been distorted by contemporary
abuses, the instinct frequently loses its ability to function for
either purpose. This destruction of libido may be appreciated by
some "population-control zealots." Procreation would no longer
be a problem and population would decrease without the need for
birth control pills, vasectomies, or abortions.

4.

Regarding the commission's recommendation for sex education, Sweden's experience should be noted. Sex education, the
type the educators have in mind, has existed in Sweden since
1954. On March 1, 1964, the Los Angeles *Times* reported: "The
King's physician, Dr. Ulf Nordwall, and 140 eminent Swedish
doctors and teachers signed a petition to their government expressing concern over sexual hysteria in the young. The petition
asserted that this problem appeared to be a product of sex education, and it was now the business of the schools to correct it."

5.

The Presidential Commission stated that "sexually emancipated,
college educated, and sexually experienced persons are less sexually aroused by obscenity and pornography." However, I fear
the commission has misinterpreted this finding. When a normal
individual is exposed to activities having sexual connotations,
sexual interests should be aroused. Eroticisms evoke memories of
childhood sensual excitations associated with voyeurism, exhibitionism, and masturbation. Pornography is sold for the purpose of stimulating sexual desire—otherwise, for what purpose
does it exist? Since all pleasures remain stored in the subconscious
mind and are never forgotten, failure to show a response when
pornography is used as a sexual stimulant indicates a sexual
disinterest. The sexually knowledgeable youth, who have been
so exposed to pornography and free love that they no longer
respond to these stimuli, are, indeed, sexually out of balance.
Their unfulfilled longings for complete sexuality cannot be met
by additional pornography and free love. The "sexually emancipated, college educated, and sexually experienced" free-lovers
referred to by the commission are, I do not doubt, immune to the
effects of pornography; but they suffer instead from psychosexual problems ranging from the disinterest described to actual
sexual impotence.

The commission's implication that exposure to pornography
and physical sexual indulgences makes one better adjusted and,

therefore, less aroused by erotic material is fallacious. It is terribly unfortunate that the Commission repeatedly draws unwarranted inferences from its investigations.

6.

It is obvious that genital anatomy is not invariably pornographic. No patient need first peer through peepholes in sex laboratories, such as those of Professors Masters and Johnson, to know that physicians medically examining genital organs are not engaging in sensual excitations. It is obvious, too, that no one needs a presidential commission to understand that when genital anatomy is used to express sexual desire carnal senses are aroused. By the same token there is no doubt that pornography and obscenity debase and harm society. In its report, the commission does not agree with these observations of ordinary mortals. After spending millions of dollars, the commission determined, for example, that:

> college-educated persons and people who are sexually experienced are less likely to be aroused by pornography. People who are older, less educated, more religious, less experienced with erotic materials, higher in guilt, or female are more likely to judge a given erotic stimulus obscene.

Again, the commission's deductions cannot be substantiated clinically. Medical experiences show that the older, "less educated" married couples—whose parents often lacked funds to keep them in college nurseries after high school graduation—are, ordinarily, more sexually adjusted than the commission's "sexually experienced, pornographically immune" college-educated subjects. As previously mentioned, pornography exists for the purpose of lewdness and requires a regression to exhibitionism and voyeurism. The normal person resents public intrusions into his sex life. His resentment and shame are natural attempts to protect himself from the pervert's delights. The older individual, described by the commission, in finding erotic material obscene, is showing a natural reaction; the commission's college students' lack of response, I find, reflects evidence of impotence and perversity.

If mature persons are to maintain sexual adjustments, they must not relinquish their observations, personal feelings, and judgments in reference to the wild scholasticisms of academicians and the propaganda of pornographers.

7.

Just a brief comment concerning the commission's conclusion that because of social condition women fail to respond to pornography in the manner of men. This misleading assumption is far removed from an understanding of female psychology. For reference on this matter, may I suggest Helene Deutsch's book, *Psychology of Women*. Dr. Deutsch clearly explains the reasons for the difference in response between the two sexes.

Sincerely,
Melvin Anchell, M.D., ABFP

XXXII

~~~~~~

The Perverts' Revolution
and the Law

Revolutions are in vogue.

Overthrowing opposition that does not fit one's wishes has become a familiar life style. More than ever before, revolution is the milieu in which we live.

A revolution which is spreading like a pestilence across every stratum of society is the "sexual revolution." I was first introduced to this phrase several years ago while watching television. A commercial announced that later in the evening there would be a commentary discussing the sexual revolution.

A sexual revolution seemed as incongruous as a revolt against the natural function of the digestive system or against using the eyes for visual perception. Nevertheless, a revolution was in progress. Sexual revolutionists were demanding that sexual gratifications be fulfilled without restraints and, to a large extent, through the use of visual, oral, and anal organs as well as the genital ones. According to the revolutionaries, free love and sexual deviation are the order of the day. The proposals made are not those for a sexual revolution; more to the point, they are for a sexual plague. Disseminating this sexual plague are deviates who have failed to achieve sexual maturity and whose sexual pleasures are contingent on infantile self-love pampered with childhood sexual regressions. The sexual revolt is, indeed, a revolution—the perverts' revolution. Deviants find it easy to infect the young, the radical libertines, and the avant-garde that are sympathetic to them. Overwhelmed by this tolerance, perverts cannot find enough ways to indulge their delights. They are determined to keep and extend their new-found acceptance. They interpret the open privileges allowed them as a mandate to convert society to their ways. Normal persons squeamish about perversion are accused of having "hang-ups." Anyone questioning perversity is regarded as a Victorian ultraconservative or a victim of Judeo-Christian ethics.

To guard against any encroachments, the pervert finds it essential to denigrate the normal human sexual needs that are foreign to him. Psychoanalysis reveals that he subconsciously fears controls over pornography and perversion as attempts to castrate him.

Pornography embellishes the deviant's sex acts. From the pulpit of pornography, the pervert espouses his revolution and spreads the gospel of perversion.

While this steady erosion of defenses is taking place, the pornographic media continues its never-relenting force feedings of debased sex. No one is immune to the ravages of the pornographic bombardment. Pornography may be enjoyed initially as a sensual spice until eventually the person becomes hooked on its addictive qualities. The process by which sexual regression occurs is observable by the manifest changes which take place within the individual as a result of obscenities.

The normal individual appears unaware of the contamination to which he is subjected. He finds himself figuratively immersed in an atmosphere of pornography. In private homes, at cocktail parties, in bars, in many forms of social entertainment, he finds the unnatural has become fashionable.

Sexual contamination especially affects the behavior of youths. Court and legal decisions handed down in pornography cases tend to mislead them further. They learn that pornography is protected under the guise of safeguarding "accepted community standards" and "socially redeeming values." The courts' interpretations confuse not only young people but community leaders who ostensibly accept the new standards on the grounds of openness and frankness.

After testifying in a recent case in California, I received the following letter advising me of the jury's decision:

Office of
CITY ATTORNEY
Criminal Division
2005 South Broadway
Los Angeles 12, California
Roger Arnebergh
City Attorney
May 15, 1969

Dr. Melvin Anchell
11633 San Vicente Boulevard
Los Angeles, California
Dear Dr. Anchell:

You have probably read in the newspapers that the jury found all defendants guilty in the first "bottomless case" tried by the City of Los Angeles. The Los Angeles *Times* Editorial Page of May 13, 1969, commenting on the case stated, "It was the first successful prosecution against operators of a 'bottomless bar' in the State of California."

I wish to extend to you my gratitude for having the courage to testify in this sensitive area and for helping the City of Los Angeles in their prosecution of this case.

Very truly yours,

Roger Arnebergh   Stuart Goldfarb
City Attorney   Deputy City Attorney

Almost immediately the conviction of this topless-bottomless dancer and her nightclub manager was reversed by the Appellate Court. The court said in part: ". . . we cannot assume that jurors in themselves necessarily express or reflect community standards; we must achieve so far as possible the application of an objective, rather than a subjective determination of community standards. . . .

"To sanction convictions without expert evidence of community standards encourages a jury to condemn as obscene such conduct or material as is personally distasteful or offensive to the particular juror."

It is an interesting comparison to note the published opinion of Dr. Karl A. Menninger. Dr. Menninger said that he considers guilt, competence, and responsibility to be moral questions and not medical ones. "The judge and jury are the community's representatives in this area. It is for them to make judgment and apply the sanctions appropriate, not us psychiatrists."

The term "socially redeeming," as used by the courts, serves as an overall coverage for pornographers. For example, the stage musical *Hair* is an admixture of socially redeeming lyrics borrowed from Shakespeare combined with voyeurism and exhibitionism. The public is gulled into accepting the musical as art because of its minuscule borrowings from Shakespeare. If nightclubs served patrons contaminated food and beverages, there are laws that would close them down. But when patrons are served material causing emotional disorders—in essence, a kind of psychological venereal disease— the courts appear unconcerned and hide behind the hollowness of "objective community standards." It is as if a playgoer went to an elegant restaurant where he was served tidbits of steak smothered with slime. If the comparision is offensive, how much more so is the pornographic smut inflicted on normal individuals by those in power in the entertainment media! The courts' actions uphold the rights of the sexual pervert through the media of pornography at the expense of contaminating those who are not perverted.

It is the mature individual, who has not regressed and who is determined not to have his sexuality disrupted, whose way of life is in greatest jeopardy. It is he who must aid in reversing the trend brought about by the perverts' revolution.

The problem is acute. Either our society accepts the tenets of the perverts and becomes a free-love bastion, or we protect our way of life by supporting mature sexuality. There can be no compromise. Perversion and mature love cannot exist side by side. Each destroys the other.

XXXIII

~~~~~~

Morality versus Reality

Fundamentally, the force that rules the world is conduct, whether it be moral or immoral. If it is moral, at
least there may be hope for the world. If immoral,
there is not only no hope, but no prospect of anything
but destruction of all that has been accomplished dur-
in the last five thousand years.

—Nicholas Murray Butler

Although the discussions in this book are not concerned with
morality in the usual sense of the word, there is a natural,
instinctive morality that keeps pace with human evolution.
This basic morality is very pertinent to our problem. To
decry its dictates as an obsolete man-made system is to decry
all other matters pertaining to instincts.

Natural morality evolves with the social order. The morality which served human needs during the periods of
patriarchal domination became obsolete of itself when human
society progressed to a more advanced stage. Much of the
morality which applied during the Victorian era is obsolete
today. But today, as before, instinctive morality serves as
man's guide for compliance with natural laws in making his
adjustment for survival in his present environment. It is
essential for the life instincts.

It is this basic, instinctive morality which is the safeguard against the current excessive overswing toward perversion. In line with the present state of human evolution, today's morality requires more than a mere physical relationship in adult human sexuality. In the sexual development of the child, it does not tolerate sexual molestation by an adult, whether it be by an individual or by the mass assault of entertainment media. In this connection, it is encouraging to note that a decent movie, the delightfully wholesome Walt Disney film *Mary Poppins*, reported higher box office receipts as of 1966 than any other film since its release and rates as one of the four all-time top-grossing films in the world.

The apparent tolerance of perversion today arises, I believe, from an abreaction against intolerance. The first natural reaction of the normal person toward the pervert is one of disgust—to shun the abnormal, as a subconscious protective defense against contamination. Yet because normal behavior and perverted behavior arise from the same universal instincts, there has developed a humanitarian effort to understand and sympathize with the unfortunate creature whose instincts have been perverted. As a result, laws have been modified, allowing perverts greater freedom of expression and action. The humanitarian motive is commendable, but it has now gone overboard in an abreaction of tolerance for perversion that is contaminating normal individuals to an alarming degree. More and more the sexual attitudes of the younger, more vulnerable generation are being confused, and they are being led to believe that perverse expressions of sexuality are normal instead of abnormal. It is time for humanitarian concern to swing away from the pervert and direct sympathy and efforts toward rescuing his victims and protecting the society upon whom he inflicts his perversions.

Already in the early 1970s the pendulum is beginning to swing back toward normalcy. Basic needs will not allow average, normal individuals to accept perversion permanently. They may experiment—but they must inevitably return to

288 Sex and Sanity

the normal, because perverted sexuality does not satisfy the human sexual instinct. The continued tension, confusion, and guilt feelings caused by an overdose of perversion bring on a mental nausea. The situation is like that of a child in a candy store, who at first guzzles all he can of the forbidden sweets and then becomes violently sick and upchucks the whole mess.

The overemphasis on the sex act itself has made man more aware of the true, full meaning of human sexuality and of the need for love. The overswing to violence has awakened a new realization of the need to expand personal love into a love for all humanity.

Within the past century—less than a moment in evolutionary time—human progress toward freedom has been greatly accelerated by the participation of women and children in the traditional revolt of the young males. Although this change is now apparent in our Western civilization, it has not yet occurred throughout the human race. Nevertheless, the world senses this change and its promise of greater freedom. Therefore the antagonism of youth is directed against the various forms of authority which will try to dominate by physical strength. Hence the protests against war, for example—not always wisely carried out, but motivated by youth's desire to fulfill its newly awakened awareness of "the brotherhood of man."

The old line "authoritative authority"—which dominates with varying degrees of sadism and chiefly for its own benefit —has been unable to cope with the rebellion of this generation. Unfortunately, this failure has caused a large segment of adult authority to overswing in the opposite direction—that of relinquishing all attempts to control or discipline the young. This extreme only serves to confuse young people all the more. *Youth needs and wants to be given a sense of direction by adult guidance.*

The evolution of authority, the social order, and morality go hand in hand. Human civilization has now evolved from the supreme rule of a personal authority to the democratic rule of the majority of the people who elect a national government, and it has made a step toward realizing the international brotherhood of man in the United Nations.

Eventually, there will evolve a human society in which man can live in peace with himself and his fellow men without controls other than his own highly developed moral instincts. But that day is in the far distant future.

In the meantime, mankind is making another small advance toward this ultimate goal—a slow and painful step, but forward. As poet-philosopher Kahlil Gibran says in *The Prophet*:

Even those who limp go not backward.

XXXIV

~~~~~~~~~~~~~~~~~~~~~~~~~~~~~~~~~~~~~~~

What Is Love?

Through the ages, love has baffled definition by poets, philosophers, and ordinary mortals. Each has had his own interpretation—and each, in his own way, has no doubt been correct. As with everything else connected with the human being, the meaning of love itself evolves—both with the evolution of the race and with the development of each individual's understanding of life.

Shall I then, out of my own experience—both personal and clinical—try to define love in the context of our present reality?

Human sexuality today, to be complete, must fulfill the highest needs of the individual as well as that of perpetuating the species. The essential ingredients—affectionate love and the helpmate quality—have become more significant for this purpose than the physical sex act. The mere act of copulation does not signify love. But, when the essential ingredient is present, the fusion of man and woman becomes an ecstasy of union expressive of their love. This union, however, cannot be completely expressed, in our present society, unless the partners are married, because marriage provides the symbol that each considers the other's happiness and welfare the most important thing in the world.

Love, then, is the complete fulfillment of human sexuality between man and wife. It is a many-faceted experience.

Each partner feels a release of mental tension and a sense of pleasure at the sight, touch, smell, or sound of the other. Each feels joy when the other is near, or unexpectedly appears at the place of work, on the street, and other places. When one sees the other after even a short separation, it is with the freshness of the first time. They feel an embarrassing but reassuring pride in each other in the presence of others. One feels the tugging of an unrequited need when the senses tell that the other is absent, and during long periods of absence this longing builds up and is only partially relieved by memories. There is a surge of relief and gladness when they meet again—a desire to express the need to protect, possess, and cherish the other as they embrace.

When they lie down together at night, each feels the need to merge with the other, this separated part—this other half. They feel the compulsion to express their love, to unite with each other, and fuse into one being. This union releases bound-up tensions, casting these out, and bringing a deep sense of peace.

There is an intolerance, too, in their love—an intolerance of sharing this intimate relationship with anyone else.

Out of this union, however, comes another human being— small, dependent—and with this child of their union they share their love gladly, because in so doing it enriches their own. There is a different quality to this parent-child love— less intimate, less possessive, more protective—and, in a way, it is more universal. Through their child, the parents have become a part of all humanity, of the stream of life—past, present, and future. The child represents their tangible immortality.

From this parent-child love, personal yet universal, evolves the ultimate extension of love to all mankind. As yet, the complete realization of this love is a distant, unrealized utopia. Man has not yet learned "to love his neighbor as himself," although the possibility of achieving this goal has been demonstrated from time to time throughout history by such great teachers as Moses, Plato, Jesus, Buddha, Confucius, Mohammed, and Gandhi. Unfortunately, the wisdom of such leaders is nearly always misinterpreted by their disciples, who identify these teachings with their own more limited experiences. Mankind must therefore continue to repeat this lesson of universal love, progressing slowly each time, until the accumulated experience of evolution develops in the human species the instinct of love as the answer to life itself.

Bibliography

~~~~~~

A clinician's skill depends on the use he has made of his experience. Some learn from every case they see; others go on repeating the same mistakes to the end of their days. A doctor's chief teachers are his patients, and a man who has seen five hundred cases of pneumonia may not have the understanding of the disease which comes with the intelligent study of a score of patients.

> —Sir William Osler
> (Dean of American Medicine)

No book, no journal, and no refresher course can teach a doctor so well as the critical study of his own patients.

> —I. R. McWhinney
> (British Medical Journal
> 3:488, May 1968)

First and foremost is twenty-five years' clinical observations of my patients.

Albert, R. S., "The Role of Mass Media and the Effect of Aggressive Film Content upon Children," *Genetic Psychology Monographia:* 221–285, 1957.

Aldrich, C. R., M.D., "The Challenges of Community Psychiatry," *Image*, vol. 11, No. 8: 3–4, October 1969.

American Medical News, SIECUS, SIECOP debated; December 8, 1969.

Anchell, Melvin, M.D., "Academician Sex Hoax," *Friar* magazine: 28–39, November 1970.

—"Classroom Sex Instruction," *Journal of the Sarastota County Medical Association*, Vol. 16, No. 3, May 1969.

"Obscenity and Pornography," *The Marian:* 37–38, September 1970.

—"Obscenity in the Mail," Published Hearings before the Subcommittee on Postal Operations, Serial No. 91–93, U.S. Government Printing Office: 171–73, August 1970.

—"Psychological Effects of Sex Education in Schools," *Christian Economics:* 1, 11, October 1970.

—*Psychology of Sex, Child and Family*, vol. 8, no. 1: 81–84, Winter 1969.

—"Sexual Buffoonism," *National Reporter*—CDL, vol. VII, no. 7: p. 6, July 1970.

—"Sex Education," *Education*, vol. 90, no. 3: 241–44, March 1970.

—"Sex—Right or Left," *Public Research Institute of California*, No. 11, April 1969.

—Expert witness testimony for *State of Ohio vs. Motion Picture "Vixen,"* et. al., No. A242722.

—Expert witness testimony for Maricopa County, *Arizona vs. Motion Picture "I Am Curious (Yellow),"* et. al., No. A228092.

—"The Pervert's Revolution," *Congregationalist:* 4–7, April 1970.

—"The New Sexual Revolution," *The Texas Methodist:* January 16, 1970.

—"Urban Woman," *Survey Program*, NBC-TV, 1970.

—"Woman," *Marriage*, 29–33, January 1970.

Bandura, A. and Ross, Dorothea, "Imitation of Film-mediated Aggressive Models," *Journal of Abnormal and Social Psychology*, 3–11, 1963.

Berkowitz, L., *The Development of Motives and Values in the Child*, Basic Books, 1964.

Blumer, H., *Movies and Conduct*, Macmillan, 1953.

Christensen, H. T. and Carpenter, G. R., "Value–Behavior Discrepancies Regarding Pre-marital Coitus in Three Western Cultures," *American Sociological Review*, Vol. 22: 66–75, 1962.

Commission on Obscenity and Pornography, Report of, United States Government Printing Office, September 30, 1970.

—Report of Commissioner Charles H. Keating, Jr., 1811 Provident Tower, Cincinnati, Ohio, September 30, 1970.

Deutsch, Helene, M.D., *Psychology of Women*, Grune and Stratton, vols. 1 & 2, 1954.

Ford, C. S. and Beach, F. S., *Pattern of Sexual Behavior*, Hoeber, 1961.

Freud, Sigmund, *The Standard Edition of Complete Psychological Works of Sigmund Freud*, Hogarth Press with special reference to:
  Beyond the Pleasure Principle
  Civilization and Its Discontents
  Group Psychology and the Analysis of the Ego
  Jokes and Their Relation to the Unconscious
  Psychopathology of Everyday Life
  Sexual Enlightenment of Children
  Sexuality and the Psychology of Love
  Studies in Parapsychology
  The Interpretation of Dreams
  Therapy and Technique
  Three Essays on the Theory of Sexuality
  Totem and Taboo
  Wild Psychology

Ganz, R. H., M.D., "The Family Physician as Counselor," *Physician's Management*: 66–78, November 1969.

Henningsen, P., "Can Children Be Protected Against Indecent Assault?" *Jugendschutz*: 150–54, June 1965.

Kinsey, A. C., *Sexual Behavior in the Human Female*, W. B. Saunders, 1953.

—*Sexual Behavior in the Human Male*, W. B. Saunders, 1948.

Kirkpatrick, J., *The Smut Peddlers*, Doubleday, 1965.

Levin, Max, M.D., "Sex in the Adolescent Years," *Current Medical Digest*, September 1968.

—"Healthy Sexual Behavior," *Pediatric Clinics of North America*, vol. 16, no. 2, May 1969

—"How Mature Is the Child?" *CMD*, March 1969.

—"Pornography and Our Youngsters," *CMD*, January 1965.

—*Vassar and the Non-Virgins*, Williams and Wilkins Company, 1966.

Linner, Birgetta, *Sex and Society in Sweden*, Pantheon Books, 1967.

Los Angeles County Medical Association Bulletin, SIECOP, September 18, 1969.

Masters, W. A. & Johnson, V. E., *Human Sexual Response*, Little, Brown and Company, 1966.

Medical Insight Magazine, "The Future of Encounter Groups," vol. 2, no. 7: 66–71, July 1970.

Mendel, Werner M., M.D., "Maladjusted Psychiatry," *Medical Opinion and Review*, vol. 5, no. 3: 140–45, March 1969.

Menninger, Karl, M.D., *Man against Himself*, Harcourt Brace Jovanovich, 1938.

—*Love against Hate*, Harvest Books, 1942.

New York Academy of Medicine, "On Salacious Literature," *Bulletin of the New York Academy of Medicine*, vol. 39, no. 8: 545–46, August 1963.

New York University College of Medicine, Department of Psychiatry, unpublished lecture–demonstrations 1944.

—Kinsey, A. C., lectures.

Otto, H. A., "Sex and Violence on the American Newsstands," *Journalism Quarterly*, no. 40: 19–26, 1963.

Parlour, Richard R., M.D., "Family Life Education," unpublished SIECOP paper, September 27, 1969.

Parsons, J. M., M.D., "AMA's Erotic Samaritans," *The Journal of the Sarasota County Medical Society*, vol. 16, no. 4, July 1969.

—"Sex Education and the No-No Moralists," *SIECOP Bulletin*, October 1969.

Shainess, Natalie, M.D., Statements given before the congressional committee (regarding obscenity) U.S. Government Printing Office Serial no. 91–93, November 1970.

Sheeley, N. F., "Sex and the Practicing Physician," *Journal of American Medical Association*, 195: 133–34, 1966.

Slovenko, Ralph, *Social Behavior and the Law*, Charles Thomas Publishers, 1965.

Spock, B., *Decent and Indecent*, McCall Publishing Co., 1970.
—"How Can We Protect Our Children from Obscenity?" *Redbook* magazine, April 1965.
Talbott, John A., M.D., "Community Psychiatry," *Journal of American Medical Association*, vol. 210, no. 7: 1233–1237.
Wertham, F., M.D., "The Scientific Study of Mass Media Effects," *American Journal of Psychiatry*, no. 4: 119, 1962.
—"What Do We Know About Mass Media Effects?" *Corrective Psychiatry*, vol. 14, no. 4, Winter 1968.

Index

301

Unnatural sex life, author's opinion of, 35-36
  free love, 42-43
Unstructured relationships, 36-38
Uppers, 86
Urethra, 129, 132, 137
Urinating, 121-22, 132
Urine, 137
Uterine tubes, 191
Uterus, 123, 130, 144
  hysterectomies and, 172
  reproductive cycle and, 162-66

Vagina, 123
  douching and, 147-48
  inflamation of, 132
  stimulation of, 129-30
Vaginal constriction, 38, 130
Vaginal sensations, 121
Valenti, Jack, 272
Venereal disease, 152-57
Virginity, 159-61
Voyeurism, 84, 205, 259-61
  exhibitionism and, 228-31

Watson, Tex, 89
Watts riots (1965), 91-92
Wet dreams, 37
What Price Sex Education? (Hill), 251
"When a Man Marries" (Collins), 118*n*
Whitman, Charles, 108

Wife swapping, 204-205
Withdrawal, 146
Without a Stitch, 268
Womb, 59
Women, 23, 158-76
  author's opinion of love and unstructured relationships of, 36-38
  author's opinion of role of mating instinct of, 42-43
  author's opinion of sexual emancipation of, 35-36
  clinical sexual truths, 48-49
  female responses, 120-26
  menopause, 170-72
  menstruation and pregnancy, 162-69
  monogamy and, 138-40
  orgasm of, 14, 16, 48-49, 129-30
  sex-linked psychological trauma of, 38-40
  sterilization and, 149-50
  surgery of, 172-75
  virginity, 159-61
World War I, 79
World War II, 79, 108

Yippies, 81
Young people, sexual needs of, 9-20
Youth, 255-57
Youth crime, 80

Zeus, 110-11